MEI STRUCTURED MATHEMATICS

SECOND EDITION

Pure Mathematics 4

Terry Heard
David Martin

Series Editor: Roger Porkess

Hodder & Stoughton

A MEMBER OF THE HODDER HEADLINE GROUP

Acknowledgements

We are grateful to the following companies, institutions and individuals who have given permission to reproduce photographs in this book. Every effort has been made to trace and acknowledge ownership of copyright. The publishers will be glad to make suitable arrangements with any copyright holders whom it has not been possible to contact.

OCR, AQA and Edexcel accept no responsibility whatsoever for the accuracy or method of working in the answers given.

Orders: please contact Bookpoint Ltd, 130 Milton Park, Abingdon, Oxon OX14 4SB. Telephone: (44) 01235 827720, Fax: (44) 01235 400454. Lines are open from 9.00–6.00, Monday to Saturday, with a 24 hour message answering service. You can also order through our website at www.hodderheadline.co.uk

British Library Cataloguing in Publication Data
A catalogue record for this title is available from the The British Library

ISBN 0 340 804343

First published 1995
Second edition published 2001
Impression number   10 9 8 7 6 5 4 3 2
Year   2006 2005 2004 2003 2002

Copyright © 1995, 2001 Terry Heard, David Martin

Typeset by Pantek Arts Ltd, Maidstone, Kent.
Printed in Great Britain for Hodder & Stoughton Educational, a division of Hodder Headline Plc, 338 Euston Road, London NW1 3BH by Martins the Printers Ltd, Berwick upon Tweed.

MEI Structured Mathematics

Mathematics is not only a beautiful and exciting subject in its own right but also one that underpins many other branches of learning. It is consequently fundamental to the success of a modern economy.

MEI Structured Mathematics is designed to increase substantially the number of people taking the subject post-GCSE, by making it accessible, interesting and relevant to a wide range of students.

It is a credit accumulation scheme based on 45 hour modules which may be taken individually or aggregated to give Advanced Subsidiary (AS) and Advanced GCE (A Level) qualifications in Mathematics, Further Mathematics and related subjects (like Statistics). The modules may also be used to obtain credit towards other types of qualification.

The course is examined by OCR (previously the Oxford and Cambridge Schools Examination Board) with examinations held in January and June each year.

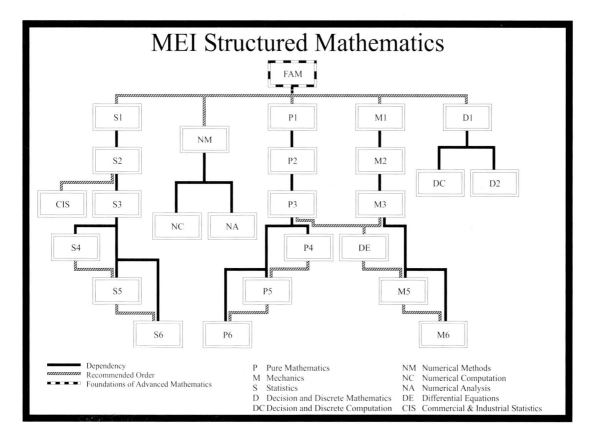

This is one of the series of books written to support the course. Its position within the whole scheme can be seen in the diagram above.

Mathematics in Education and Industry is a curriculum development body which aims to promote the links between Education and Industry in Mathematics at secondary level, and to produce relevant examination and teaching syllabuses and support material. Since its foundation in the 1960s, MEI has provided syllabuses for GCSE (or O Level), Additional Mathematics and A Level.

For more information about MEI Structured Mathematics or other syllabuses and materials, write to MEI Office, Albion House, Market Place, Westbury, Wiltshire, BA13 3DE.

Introduction

This is the fourth in the series covering the pure mathematics of the MEI Structured Mathematics course. It is supported by additional on-line materials available through the MEI distance learning programme. For further details please e-mail the MEI office: Office@mei.org.uk.

You may be using this book as the final pure component of an A level course, or as a continuation into AS or A level Further Mathematics. In either case, you will have already come across a wide spread of pure mathematics. Two of the chapters here (Vector geometry, and Graphs and inequalities) take some of these ideas further; two other (Complex numbers and Matrices) introduce new topics. The chapters on proof and induction, which are rather different in character, are intended to give you an opportunity to deepen your understanding of what mathematics is about, and to look more carefully at the development of mathematical arguments. This is not always easy, but it is worth tackling seriously, since it underpins the whole of the subject.

In writing the first edition of this book we were helped by family, friends and colleagues. In particular we are grateful to Mike Jones, Diana Cowey, James Griffin and Roger Porkess for their suggestions. Most influential have been our students: their existence goaded us into getting on with the writing, and their comments (or sometimes confusions) helped us to improve the drafts. It is a pleasure to record our thanks to them all.

This second edition of *Pure Mathematics 4* has been prepared by Terry Heard, with valuable assistance from Richard Lissaman. The order of topics has been changed to make the earlier sections more accessible, particularly for those who have to start *Pure Mathematics 4* before completing *Pure Mathematics 1* to *3*. More past examination questions have been included, and to make room for these some extensions beyond the component criteria have been omitted.

Finally we would like to thank the various examination boards who have given permission for their past questions to be used in the exercises.

Terry Heard and David Martin

Contents

Appendix: the scalar triple product   151

Answers   157

Index   178

1

Proof

I have discovered a truly marvellous proof of this, but the margin is too narrow to contain it.

Fermat, 1637

The language of proof

By now you have learnt many mathematical skills and associated strategies for using them to solve problems. Before moving on to further techniques and methods it is worth pausing to consider again the fundamental idea of proof in mathematics. This is important because:

- you need careful reasoning to ensure correct conclusions

- it is often satisfying to sort out the connections between familiar facts and new ones

- a well-constructed proof is an efficient and persuasive way of communicating with others.

Here is an example of a statement about a natural number (i.e. a positive integer) n.

If the natural number n is a multiple of 3 then n^2 is a multiple of 9.

Your experience of arithmetic suggests very strongly that this statement is true. You may begin to check it for certain values of n. When $n = 3, 6, 9, 12$, it is certainly true. However, how can you be sure that the statement is true for *all* multiples of 3? You cannot check them all, there are infinitely many! Even if you check the statement for the first 100,000 multiples of 3 there are still infinitely many multiples of 3 left to check. To check a statement that applies to infinitely many natural numbers for a finite number of cases does not constitute a proof; you simply have not checked all the cases.

In mathematics we call a statement which we suspect to be true a *conjecture*. To be sure that the above conjecture is true for all natural numbers n, you must look for some deeper generic reason that the statement is true rather than just checking individual cases. You may notice that

$$6 = 2 \times 3 \text{ and so } 6^2 = 2 \times 3 \times 2 \times 3 = 2 \times 2 \times 3 \times 3 = 4 \times 9$$

$$9 = 3 \times 3 \text{ and so } 9^2 = 3 \times 3 \times 3 \times 3 = 9 \times 9$$

$$12 = 4 \times 3 \text{ and so } 12^2 = 4 \times 3 \times 4 \times 3 = 4 \times 4 \times 3 \times 3 = 16 \times 9.$$

This may give you an idea for a proof. A proof is often discovered following a search for common patterns through a detailed investigation of various cases of the conjecture. The example above is, of course, a very simple example of this.

Here is a proof of the conjecture above. This illustrates how a proof of a conjecture is a chain of reasoning which begins at the given starting point, leads in logical steps or deductions and ends by establishing the truth of the conjecture. If we have a proof which establishes the truth of a mathematical conjecture we then call that conjecture a *theorem*.

THEOREM

If the natural number n is a multiple of 3 then n^2 is a multiple of 9.

PROOF

Suppose that the natural number n is a multiple of 3. Then n can be written as $3m$ where m is a natural number. Hence we have that

$$n^2 = n \times n = 3m \times 3m = 3 \times 3 \times m \times m = 9m^2.$$

This shows that n^2 is a multiple of 9.

Note

This proof can easily be *generalised* to prove the following:

Theorem: **if the natural number *n* is a multiple of the natural number *k* then n^2 is a multiple of k^2.**

There are essentially three steps in the above proof.

1 If n is a multiple of 3 then $n = 3m$ where m is a natural number.

2 If $n = 3m$ then $n^2 = 9m^2$

3 If $n^2 = 9m^2$ then n^2 is a multiple of 9.

Notice that these three statements all have the same structure:

'if the statement P is true then it follows that the statement Q is true'.

This can be abbreviated to:

'P implies Q' or symbolically '$P \Rightarrow Q$' (or mathematicians sometimes say 'if P then Q').

Notice that the soundness of the step '$P \Rightarrow Q$' does not depend on whether P is in fact true. For example the argument 'petrol costs £15 per litre $\Rightarrow$ 10 litres of petrol cost £150'

is valid whatever the actual price of petrol.

The statement '$P \Rightarrow Q$' can also be written as '$Q \Leftarrow P$' ('Q is implied by P'). But you need to be careful not to confuse the statement '$P \Rightarrow Q$' with its *converse* '$P \Leftarrow Q$': these are not saying the same thing and sometimes the converse of a true statement is false. For example:

'Mary was born in Edinburgh $\Rightarrow$ Mary was born in Scotland'

is true, but the converse

'Mary was born in Edinburgh $\Leftarrow$ Mary was born in Scotland'

is false.

When '$P \Rightarrow Q$' and '$P \Leftarrow Q$' are both true we say that 'P is equivalent to Q' and write '$P \Leftrightarrow Q$'. This is commonly abbreviated to 'P if and only if Q'.

Suppose the statement P is '$x = 2$' and the statement Q is '$x^2 = 4$'. Clearly if P is true then Q is true. However if Q is true then P may not be true because we may have that $x = -2$. Thus '$P \Rightarrow Q$' is true but '$P \Leftarrow Q$' is not true and so '$P \Leftrightarrow Q$' is also not true.

However, if R is the statement '$x = 2$ or $x = -2$' then '$R \Leftrightarrow Q$' is true.

The following table summarises all that has been said so far and the column on the right gives some rather formal language that mathematicians sometimes use to describe these ideas.

Meaning	Abbreviation	Symbolically	Formal terminology
If P is true then Q is true	If P then Q	$P \Rightarrow Q$	P is a sufficient condition for Q *or* P implies Q *or* P only if Q
If Q is true then P is true	If Q then P	$P \Leftarrow Q$	P is a necessary condition for Q *or* P is implied by Q *or* P if Q
If P is true then Q is true *and* if Q is true then P is true	If P then Q and if Q then P	$P \Leftrightarrow Q$	P is a necessary and sufficient condition for Q *or* P is equivalent to Q *or* P if and only if Q

The importance of distinguishing between $\Rightarrow$ and $\Leftrightarrow$ is shown in the following example.

EXAMPLE 1.1   Solve the equation $x = 6 + \sqrt{x}$.

SOLUTION

$$x = 6 + \sqrt{x}$$
$$\Leftrightarrow \quad x - 6 = \sqrt{x}$$
$$\Rightarrow \quad (x-6)^2 = x \qquad\qquad ①$$
$$\Leftrightarrow \quad x^2 - 12x + 36 = x$$
$$\Leftrightarrow \quad x^2 - 13x + 36 = 0$$
$$\Leftrightarrow \quad (x-9)(x-4) = 0$$
$$\Leftrightarrow \quad x = 9 \text{ or } x = 4.$$

This argument shows that the only possible roots of the original equation are 9 or 4, but since the squaring step ① is not reversible (as shown by using $\Rightarrow$ rather than $\Leftrightarrow$) you must test these possibilities by substitution: since $9 = 6 + \sqrt{9}$ but $4 \neq 6 + \sqrt{4}$ you conclude that 9 is the only root.

Here is another example of mathematical proof. This time the statement is a familiar property of angles inscribed in a circle. Notice that again it is impossible to check this statement for all possible circles by drawing and measuring. Firstly, there are infinitely many circles; secondly you cannot measure angles (or anything else!) with 100% accuracy.

THEOREM

The angle subtended at the centre of a circle by an arc is twice the angle subtended at a point on the rest of the circumference by the same arc.

In other words $\angle AOC = 2 \angle ABC$ in figure 1.1.

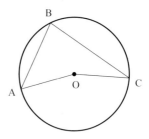

Figure 1.1

PROOF

In figure 1.2 the lengths of AO, BO and CO must all be the same because they are all radii of the circle.

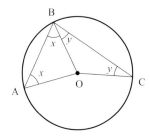

Figure 1.2

So the triangles AOB and BOC are both isosceles. Thus the angles ∠OAB and ∠OBA are equal and the angles ∠OCB and ∠OBC are equal.

Suppose that   ∠OAB = ∠OBA = $x°$ and ∠OCB = ∠OBC = $y°$.
Then   ∠ABC = ∠ABO + ∠OBC = $(x + y)°$.   ⊛
Also   ∠AOB = $(180 - 2x)°$ and ∠BOC = $(180 - 2y)°$.

The sum of the angles AOB, BOC and AOC is 360°. This gives

$$\begin{aligned}∠AOC &= (360 - ∠AOB - ∠BOC)° \\ &= [360 - (180 - 2x) - (180 - 2y)]° \\ &= (360 - 180 - 180 + 2x + 2y)° \\ &= [2(x + y)]° \\ &= 2∠ABC.\end{aligned}$$

Note

Although this proof seems convincing it is in fact incomplete. The problem is that figure 1.1 shows particular positions for A, B and C. In some other possible positions the diagram looks very different, and the proof has to be modified at line ⊛ and subsequently. This is explored in Question 10 of Exercise 1A.

Proof in mathematics

The use of proof is one of the special characteristics of mathematics: in other subjects conclusions are based on evidence or opinion, and may have to be rejected or revised in the light of new evidence. So, for example, in physics Einstein's theory of relativity superseded Newton's theory of gravitation, which had been accepted for over 200 years, because relativity can account for observed facts which Newton's theory cannot explain. Both Newton and Einstein used mathematics extensively in their work, but for a physical theory it is the experimental evidence that is crucial, and there is always the possibility that new evidence may call for changes of theory. In mathematics, however, once a theorem is properly proved you can be absolutely sure of its truth.

What does 'proof' mean **(i)** in criminal law, **(ii)** in civil law? Does proof play a part in medical research, or economics, or weather forecasting?

The central role of proof in mathematics was first recognised by the Greeks, probably as early as 400 BC. About a century later Euclid of Alexandria wrote a geometry and arithmetic text called *The Elements*. For more than 2000 years this was held to be a perfect example of how a body of mathematics could be organised into a logical system. Some 120 years ago you would probably have been using *The Elements* as one of your textbooks. Here is one of Euclid's classic proofs (Book IX, Proposition 20), preceded by an activity to get you going.

ACTIVITY

Let the primes be p_1, p_2, p_3, ... in order of size (so that $p_1 = 2$, $p_2 = 3$, $p_3 = 5$, ...), and let $X_k = p_1 p_2 ... p_k + 1$. Work out X_1, X_2, X_3, ... until you reach the first X_k which is not prime (or further if you like). Notice that each X_k is either prime or has a prime factor larger than the corresponding p_k.

THEOREM

There are infinitely many prime numbers or, in Euclid's words, prime numbers are more than any assigned multitude of prime numbers.

PROOF

1 Suppose there is just a finite number of primes, n say, and let these primes be p_1, p_2, ..., p_n.

2 Form the number $X = p_1 p_2 ... p_n + 1$.

3 If X is a prime number then it is a prime larger than any of the n primes, so there are more than n primes.

4 If X is not a prime number then it must be exactly divisible by a prime. But this prime divisor is not p_1 or p_2 or ... or p_n, since when each of these divides X there is remainder 1. Hence there must be some other prime divisor, and so again there are more than n primes.

Options **3** and **4** are the only possibilities, and each of them contradicts **1**. Therefore **1** is false, and so there are infinitely many primes.

Proof by contradiction

One powerful general method of showing that a statement P is true is to prove that P cannot be false. To do this we suppose that P is false and show that this leads to a contradiction. This is illustrated by Euclid's proof above, where P is the statement 'there are infinitely many prime numbers'. Step **1** is to suppose that P is

. false, then steps **3** and **4** show that this always leads to a contradiction. The conclusion is that P cannot be false, and hence that P must be true.

This method is called *proof by contradiction*; you may also find it described in Latin as *reductio ad absurdum* (reduction to the absurd). Here are two more examples, one a very straightforward preliminary (called a *lemma*), the other of crucial importance in the history of mathematics (see page 12).

LEMMA

An even perfect square is the square of an even integer.

PROOF

Notice first exactly what we have to prove: it is very easy to show that the square of an even number is even, since $(2k)^2 = 4k^2$ which is a multiple of 2, but here we want the converse. We have to eliminate the possibility that an even square could arise from squaring an odd number.

Any odd number can be written in the form $2k + 1$, where k is an integer. The square of this odd number is then

$$(2k + 1)^2 = 4k^2 + 4k + 1 = 2(2k^2 + 2k) + 1$$

which is odd. So if n^2 is even n cannot be odd, so n is even.

THEOREM

$\sqrt{2}$ is irrational (i.e. cannot be written as a fraction).

PROOF

Suppose that $\sqrt{2}$ is not irrational, i.e. that $\sqrt{2} = \frac{p}{q}$, where p and q are integers with no common factor (i.e. the fraction $\frac{p}{q}$ has been cancelled down to its lowest terms).

$$
\begin{aligned}
\sqrt{2} = \frac{p}{q} &\Rightarrow p^2 = 2q^2 \quad \text{(by definition of } \sqrt{2}\text{)} \qquad\qquad ① \\
&\Rightarrow p^2 \text{ is even} \\
&\Rightarrow p \text{ is even} \quad \text{(by the lemma)} \\
&\Rightarrow p = 2r \quad \text{(where } r \text{ is the integer } \tfrac{p}{2}\text{)} \\
&\Rightarrow p^2 = 4r^2 \\
&\Rightarrow 2q^2 = 4r^2 \quad \text{(from ①)} \\
&\Rightarrow q^2 = 2r^2 \\
&\Rightarrow q^2 \text{ is even} \\
&\Rightarrow q \text{ is even} \quad \text{(by the lemma again)} \\
&\Rightarrow p \text{ and } q \text{ have the common factor 2.}
\end{aligned}
$$

This contradicts the supposition that $\sqrt{2}$ could be written as a fraction in its lowest terms. Hence $\sqrt{2}$ is irrational.

Note

Be on your guard against using proof by contradiction unnecessarily. Beginners sometimes produce a proof of a statement *P* on the following lines:

1 They suppose *P* is false.

2 They then give a direct proof of *P*.

3 They note that **2** shows that supposition **1** is false.

4 They conclude that this proves, by contradiction, that *P* is true.

Clearly there is no need for **1**, **3** or **4** if a direct proof can be found in **2** – but it is not always so easy to spot this when you are involved with the detail. The message is to pay attention to the logical structure of your work as well as getting the details right.

Counter-examples and verifications

In order to prove that a general statement is *not* true all you have to do is to find one particular case for which the statement is false. Such a case is called a *counter-example*. When investigating a statement you may find many cases for which the statement is true, but these *verifications* are not enough to prove the statement, since there may still be a counter-example that you have not yet found. Sometimes however, a theorem can be proved by verifying *all possible* cases, as in the following example.

EXAMPLE 1.2

Prove that every prime number greater than 3 is of the form $6n \pm 1$, where *n* is a positive integer. Investigate the converse.

SOLUTION

No integer can be more than 3 away from a multiple of 6, so that every positive integer greater than 3 can be expressed as $6n$ or $6n \pm 1$ or $6n \pm 2$ or $6n + 3$, where *n* is a positive integer. None of $6n$, $6n \pm 2$ or $6n + 3$ is prime, since these are divisible by 6, 2 or 3 respectively. Therefore every prime greater than 3 is of the form $6n \pm 1$.

The converse states that every number of the form $6n \pm 1$ is a prime greater than 3. This is false, as shown by the counter-example $6 \times 4 + 1 = 25$, which is not prime.

Historical note

One famous counter-example took 100 years to find. In 1640 the French lawyer and great mathematician Pierre de Fermat claimed that the numbers $F_n = 2^{2^n} + 1$ are prime for all integers $n \geqslant 0$. He knew that the first five numbers, 3, 5, 17, 257, 65 537, are all prime, and he had failed after extensive searching to find any factor of the next, $F_5 = 2^{2^5} + 1 = 4\,294\,967\,297$. He wrote: 'I do not have an exact proof, but I have excluded such a large quantity of divisors by infallible proofs, and I have such great insights (*lumières*) which establish my thought that I should be sorry to retract'. But despite his confidence Fermat was wrong, though it was not until 1739 that an even greater mathematician, Leonhard Euler (1707–83), discovered that F_5 is divisible by 641.

EXERCISE 1A

1 Insert the correct symbol ($\Rightarrow$, $\Leftarrow$ or $\Leftrightarrow$) between these statements.

(i) $\theta = \dfrac{3\pi}{4}$ ... $\tan\theta = -1$

(ii) $x^2 - 5x + 4 = 0$ ... $x = 4$

(iii) **a.b** $= 0$ ... **a** is perpendicular to **b**

(iv) $\sqrt{x} = 32$ ... $x^{-\frac{1}{5}} = 0.25$

(v) $y = \sin x$ ... $\dfrac{dy}{dx} = \cos x$

(vi) $x^2 < 100$ ... $|x| < 10$

2 Given these statements about a positive integer n

> P: n is a multiple of 3
> Q: n is a multiple of 9
> R: the sum of the digits of n is a multiple of 3
> S: the sum of the digits of n is a multiple of 9

state whether the following statements are correct, and where necessary give a correct version with P, Q, R, S unchanged.

(i) P if Q

(ii) Q if P

(iii) P if and only if S

(iv) R only if P

(v) S only if R

(vi) Q if and only if R.

3 For me to have a big breakfast, it is necessary and sufficient that I should not have to go to school. For me to think of a good mathematics question, it is necessary for me to have inspiration. Inspiration comes only if I have a big breakfast. If this is a good mathematics question, what do you conclude?

4 State the converse of each of the following theorems, and say whether or not the converse is true.

(i) For a polynomial P(x), if P(a) = 0 then ($x - a$) is a factor of P(x).

(ii) If a solid is a prism then the solid has a uniform cross-section.

(iii) If triangle ABC has a right angle at A then $a^2 = b^2 + c^2$.

(iv) If $y = x^n$ then $\dfrac{dy}{dx} = nx^{n-1}$.

5 Solve the equation $\sqrt{3x + 1} = 9 - x$.

6 Prove that

$$3 - \sqrt{2x + 3} = 4 + \sqrt{x + 1} \Rightarrow x = -1 \text{ or } 3.$$

What are the solutions of $3 - \sqrt{2x + 3} = 4 + \sqrt{x + 1}$?

7 Prove that a perfect square which is a multiple of 3 is the square of a multiple of 3.

8 Prove that $\sqrt{3}$ is irrational.

9 Give either a proof or a counter-example for each of the following statements about positive numbers.

   (i) Rational + irrational = irrational.

   (ii) Irrational + irrational = irrational.

   (iii) Rational × irrational = irrational.

   (iv) Irrational × irrational = irrational.

10 (i) Adapt the proof given on page 4 to prove the same theorem in the cases when

    (a) BOC is a straight line

    (b) BC intersects the radius OA

    (c) B is on the minor arc AC.

    Does this cover all the possibilities?

  (ii) Prove that the opposite angles of a cyclic quadrilateral are supplementary (i.e. $\angle$ABC + $\angle$ADC = 180° in the diagram below).

  (iii) Prove the converse of the theorem in part **(ii)**

    (i.e. $\angle$ABC + $\angle$ADC = 180° $\Rightarrow$ ABCD in cyclic).

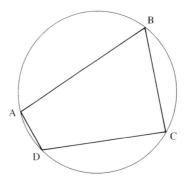

[**Hint** for part **(iii)**: Suppose not, so that D is not on the circumcircle of triangle ABC; let AD meet this circle at E; obtain a contradiction by using part **(ii)** with ABCE.]

11 Prove that if p is a prime greater than 3 then $p^2 - 1$ is a multiple of 24.

[**Hint**: Use Example 1.2.]

12 (i) By considering all the possible units digits of the positive integer n, prove that $n^5 - n$ is always divisible by 10.

  (ii) By factorising $n^5 - n$, prove that $n^5 - n$ is always divisible by 30.

13 (i) Six points are chosen in space, and each possible pair of these points is joined by a line segment. Each line segment is coloured either green or yellow. Prove that there is at least one monochrome (all green or all yellow) triangle formed by these segments.

  (ii) Investigate whether part **(i)** is true when there are five points instead of six. Justify your conclusion.

KEY POINTS

1 The flow of a proof is shown by the symbols $\Rightarrow$, $\Leftarrow$, $\Leftrightarrow$ or by the correct use of 'if', 'only if', 'necessary', 'sufficient' as follows

$P \Rightarrow Q$	P is a sufficient condition for Q	P only if Q
$P \Leftarrow Q$	P is a necessary condition for Q	P if Q
$P \Leftrightarrow Q$	P is a necessary and sufficient condition for Q	P if and only if Q

2 The converse of $P \Rightarrow Q$ is $P \Leftarrow Q$ or $Q \Rightarrow P$.

3 To prove P *by contradiction*, show that assuming P to be false leads to a contradiction.

4 A general statement can be disproved by a single *counter-example*, but cannot be proved by any number of *verifications* unless these exhaust all the possibilities.

2

Complex numbers

...that wonder of analysis, that portent of the ideal world, that amphibian between being and not-being, which we call the imaginary root of negative unity.

Leibniz, 1702

The growth of the number system

The number system with which you are familiar has taken many thousands of years to develop. In primitive societies all that are needed are the *counting numbers*, 1, 2, 3, ... (or even just the first few of these), but with the growth of trade comes the concept of a *fraction*, first recorded in a systematic way in an Egyptian papyrus of about 1650 BC.

By 500 BC the Greeks had developed ways of calculating with whole numbers and their ratios (which accounts for calling fractions *rational* numbers). They also knew that between any two fractions, however close together they might be, it is always possible to find intermediate fractions (e.g. the average of the two given fractions). So if we imagine the fractions represented by points on a number line, there is no segment of the line, however small, where there are no fractions: we express this by saying that the fractions are *dense*. Because of this the followers of Pythagoras believed that everything in geometry and in applications of mathematics could be explained in terms of rational numbers. It came as a great shock, therefore, when one of them proved that $\sqrt{2}$ is not a rational number (see page 7). Legend has it that their reaction to this threat to their beliefs was to drown the discoverer. But then Greek thinkers gradually came to terms with the existence of such *irrational* numbers, and by 370 BC Eudoxus had devised a very careful theory of proportion which included both rational and irrational numbers.

It took about another thousand years for the next major development, when the Hindu mathematician Brahmagupta (about AD 630) described *negative* numbers, and gave the usual rules for dealing with negative signs. Surprisingly, the first use of a symbol for *zero* came even later, in AD 876. This was the final element needed to complete the set of *real* numbers, consisting of positive and negative rational and irrational numbers and zero; the real numbers can be represented by the points of the *real number line*.

How did your knowledge of the number system develop? Can you think of reasons for differences from the historical order?

ACTIVITY

Draw a single Venn diagram taking {real numbers} as the universal set, and showing the following subsets: {integers}, {rational numbers}, {irrational numbers}, {positive numbers}, {negative numbers}, {zero}. Show in your diagram the numbers 3, π, $\frac{355}{113}$, -1, -1.4142, $-\sqrt{2}$.

Draw also a real number line, and mark the same numbers on it.

The number system expanded in this way because people wanted to increase the range of problems they could tackle. This can be illustrated in terms of the sorts of equation that can be solved at each stage (though of course the standard algebraic way of writing these is relatively modern).

ACTIVITY

For each of these equations make up a simple problem that would lead to the equation, and say what sort of number is needed to solve the equation.

(i) $x + 7 = 10$ **(ii)** $7x = 10$
(iii) $x^2 = 10$ **(iv)** $x + 10 = 7$
(v) $x^2 + 7x = 0$ **(vi)** $x^2 + 10 = 0$

You will have hit a snag with equation **(vi)**. Since the square of every real number is positive or zero, there is no real number whose square is -10; this is a simple example of a quadratic equation with no real roots. The existence of such equations was recognised and accepted for hundreds of years (just as the Greeks had accepted that $x + 10 = 7$ had no solution). Then two 16th century Italians, Tartaglia and Cardan, found methods of solving cubic and quartic (fourth degree) equations which forced mathematicians to take seriously the square roots of negative numbers. This required a further extension of the number system, to produce what are called *complex numbers*. These were regarded with great suspicion for many years: Descartes called them 'imaginary', Newton called them 'impossible', and Leibniz's mystification has already been quoted. But complex numbers turned out to be very useful, not least in many applications of mathematics, and had become accepted as an essential tool by the time Gauss first gave them a firm logical basis in 1831.

Working with complex numbers

Faced with the problem of wanting the square root of a negative number, we make the following Bold Hypothesis:

The real number system can be extended by including a new number, denoted by j, which combines with itself and the real numbers according to the usual laws of algebra, but which has the extra property that $j^2 = -1$.

The original notation for j was ι (the Greek letter iota); i is also commonly used instead of j.

The first thing to note is that we do not need further symbols for other square roots. For example, since $-196 = 196 \times (-1) = 14^2 \times j^2$, we see that -196 has the two square roots $\pm 14j$. The following example uses this idea in solving a quadratic equation with no real roots.

EXAMPLE 2.1

Solve the equation $z^2 - 6z + 58 = 0$, and check the roots. (We use the letter z for the variable here since we want to keep x and y to stand for *real* numbers.)

SOLUTION

Using the formula for the roots of a quadratic equation

$$z = \frac{6 \pm \sqrt{6^2 - 4 \times 58}}{2}$$

$$= \frac{6 \pm \sqrt{-196}}{2}$$

$$= \frac{6 \pm 14j}{2}$$

$$= 3 \pm 7j.$$

To check:

$$z = 3 + 7j \Rightarrow z^2 - 6z + 58 = (3 + 7j)^2 - 6(3 + 7j) + 58$$
$$= 9 + 42j + 49j^2 - 18 - 42j + 58$$
$$= 9 + 42j - 49 - 18 - 42j + 58 \quad (\text{since } j^2 = -1)$$
$$= 0.$$

Check the other root, $z = 3 - 7j$.

A number z of the form $x + yj$, where x and y are real, is called a *complex number*. In Example 2.1 you did some simple calculations with complex numbers; the general methods for addition, subtraction and multiplication are similarly straightforward.

Addition: $(x + yj) + (u + vj) = (x + u) + (y + v)j$

Subtraction: $(x + yj) - (u + vj) = (x - u) + (y - v)j$

Multiplication: $(x + yj)(u + vj) = xu + xvj + yuj + yvj^2$
$$= (xu - yv) + (xv + yu)j \quad (\text{since } j^2 = -1).$$

Division of complex numbers is dealt with in the next section.

Express the following in the form $x + y$j.

1 $(8 + 6j) + (6 + 4j)$ **2** $(9 - 3j) + (-4 + 5j)$ **3** $(2 + 7j) - (5 + 3j)$

4 $(5 - j) - (6 - 2j)$ **5** $3(4 + 6j) + 9(1 - 2j)$ **6** $3j(7 - 4j)$

7 $(9 + 2j)\left(\frac{1}{6} + \frac{1}{3}j\right)$ **8** $\left(4 - \frac{1}{2}j\right)\left(\frac{2}{3} + 2j\right)$ **9** $(7 + 3j)^2$

10 $(8 + 6j)(8 - 6j)$ **11** $(1 + 2j)(3 - 4j)(5 + 6j)$ **12** $(3 + 2j)^3$

Division of complex numbers

For the complex number $z = x + y$j, x is called the *real part* of the complex number, and y the *imaginary part*, terms introduced by Descartes in 1637. The real and imaginary parts of z are denoted by $\text{Re}(z)$ and $\text{Im}(z)$ respectively, so that, for example, if $z = 3 - 7$j then $\text{Re}(z) = 3$ and $\text{Im}(z) = -7$. Notice in particular that the imaginary part is real!

Equality of complex numbers is defined in the natural way: the complex numbers $x + y$j and $u + v$j are *equal* if $x = u$ and $y = v$.

Before you tackle the slightly more complicated problem of dividing by a complex number, you need a useful further property of equality:

$$x + yj = u + vj \Rightarrow x - u = (v - y)j \quad \text{(subtracting } u + yj \text{ from both sides)}$$
$$\Rightarrow (x - u)^2 = [(v - y)j]^2 \quad \text{(squaring both sides)}$$
$$\Rightarrow (x - u)^2 = -(v - y)^2.$$

But the squares of the real numbers $x - u$ and $v - y$ cannot be negative, so unless both sides of the final equation are zero there is a contradiction. Therefore

$$x + yj = u + vj \Rightarrow x - u = 0 \text{ and } v - y = 0$$
$$\Rightarrow x = u \quad \text{and } y = v.$$

This shows that equality of real and imaginary parts is a *necessary condition* for equality of complex numbers (as well as being a sufficient condition by definition). When we use this result we say we are *equating real and imaginary parts*.

Note

If you feel that this is making a fuss about something which is obvious, consider the similar question of the equality of rational numbers. It is true that the rational numbers $\frac{x}{y}$ and $\frac{u}{v}$ are equal if $x = u$ and $y = v$, but the converse is *not* true.

For example, $\frac{3}{2} = \frac{12}{8}$ but $3 \neq 12$ and $2 \neq 8$.

Equating real and imaginary parts is a very useful method which often yields 'two for the price of one' when working with complex numbers. The following example illustrates this.

EXAMPLE 2.2

Find real numbers p and q such that $p + qj = \dfrac{1}{3 + 5j}$.

SOLUTION

We have to find real numbers p and q such that

$$(p + qj)(3 + 5j) = 1.$$

Expanding gives $3p - 5q + (5p + 3q)j = 1$.

Equating real and imaginary parts gives

$$3p - 5q = 1$$
$$5p + 3q = 0.$$

These simultaneous equations give $p = \dfrac{3}{34}$, $q = -\dfrac{5}{34}$ and so

$$\frac{1}{3 + 5j} = \frac{3}{34} - \frac{5}{34}j.$$

ACTIVITY

Prove by a similar method that $\dfrac{1}{x + yj} = \dfrac{x - yj}{x^2 + y^2}$.

Knowing how to find a reciprocal makes other divisions straightforward.

EXAMPLE 2.3

Find the real and imaginary parts of $\dfrac{7 + 4j}{3 + 5j}$.

SOLUTION

$$\frac{7 + 4j}{3 + 5j} = (7 + 4j) \times \frac{1}{3 + 5j}$$

$$= (7 + 4j) \times \frac{3 - 5j}{34} \text{ (using the result of the previous example)}$$

$$= \frac{41 - 23j}{34}$$

so the real part is $\dfrac{41}{34}$, and the imaginary part is $-\dfrac{23}{34}$.

In practice, the easiest way to do a division is to note that

$$(x + yj)(x - yj) = x^2 - y^2j^2 = x^2 + y^2$$

which is real.

The complex number $x - yj$ is called the *complex conjugate* (or just the *conjugate*) of $x + yj$; the complex conjugate of z is denoted by z^*. To do a division you start by multiplying the numerator and the denominator by the conjugate of the denominator.

EXAMPLE 2.4

Express $\dfrac{9-4j}{2+3j}$ as a complex number.

SOLUTION

$$\frac{9-4j}{2+3j} = \frac{9-4j}{2+3j} \times \frac{2-3j}{2-3j} = \frac{18-27j-8j+12j^2}{2^2+3^2} = \frac{6-35j}{13} = \frac{6}{13} - \frac{35}{13}j$$

The corresponding general result is obtained in the same way:

$$\frac{x+yj}{u+vj} = \frac{(x+yj)(u-vj)}{(u+vj)(u-vj)} = \frac{xu+yv}{u^2+v^2} + \frac{yu-xv}{u^2+v^2}j$$

unless $u = v = 0$, in which case the division is impossible (not surprisingly, since the denominator is then zero).

 The collapse of a Bold Hypothesis
You have just avoided a mathematical inconvenience (that -1 has no real square root) by introducing a new mathematical object, j, which has the property you want: $j^2 = -1$. What happens if you try the same approach to get rid of the equally inconvenient ban on dividing by zero? The problem is that there is no real number equal to $1 \div 0$. So try making the Bold Hypothesis that you can introduce a new mathematical object which equals $1 \div 0$ but otherwise behaves like a real number. Denote this new object by ∞.

Then $1 \div 0 = \infty$, and so $1 = 0 \times \infty$.

But then you soon meet a contradiction:

$$2 \times 0 = 3 \times 0$$
$$\Rightarrow \quad (2 \times 0) \times \infty = (3 \times 0) \times \infty$$
$$\Rightarrow \quad 2 \times (0 \times \infty) = 3 \times (0 \times \infty)$$
$$\Rightarrow \quad 2 \times 1 = 3 \times 1$$
$$\Rightarrow \quad 2 = 3 \quad \text{which is impossible.}$$

So *this* Bold Hypothesis quickly leads to trouble. How can you be sure that the same will never happen with complex numbers? One way of answering this is given in *Pure Mathematics 6*; for the moment you will just have to take on trust that there is an answer, and that all is well.

EXERCISE 2B

Express the complex numbers in Questions 1–6 in the form $x + yj$.

1 $\dfrac{1}{3+j}$

2 $\dfrac{1}{6-j}$

3 $\dfrac{5j}{6-2j}$

4 $\dfrac{7+5j}{6-2j}$

5 $\dfrac{47-23j}{6+j}$

6 $\dfrac{12-8j}{(2+2j)^2}$

7 (i) Solve the equation $(2 + j)(z - 7 + 3j) = 15 - 10j$.

(ii) Solve the simultaneous equations

$$3z + 2w = 38$$
$$2z - jw = 7.$$

8 The complex numbers z and w satisfy the simultaneous equations

$$z + jw - 13$$
$$3z - 4w = 2j.$$

Find z and w, giving your answers in the form $a + bj$.

[MEI, part]

9 Expand and simplify $(a + bj)^3$. Deduce that if $(a + bj)^3$ is real then either $b = 0$ or $b^2 = 3a^2$. Hence find *all* the complex numbers z for which $z^3 = 1$.

10 Simplify **(i)** j^3; **(ii)** j^4; **(iii)** j^{37}; **(iv)** $\dfrac{1}{j}$; **(v)** $\dfrac{1}{j^{26}}$.

State a general rule for simplifying j^n, where n is any integer.

11 (i) Evaluate **(a)** $\displaystyle\sum_{r=1}^{100} j^r$; **(b)** $\displaystyle\sum_{r=-15}^{27} j^r$.

(ii) Find a condition involving the integers p and q which is true if and only if $\displaystyle\sum_{r=p}^{q} j^r = 0$.

12 (i) Expand and simplify $(a + bj)(c + dj)$.

(ii) By equating real and imaginary parts, prove that

$$(a + bj)(c + dj) = 0 \quad \Leftrightarrow \quad a = b = 0 \ \text{ or } \ c = d = 0$$

(This shows that, for complex numbers z and w, $zw = 0 \Leftrightarrow z = 0$ or $w = 0$, which is the basis of the method for solving equations by factorising.)

13 Solve
(i) $z^2 + 16 = 0$ **(ii)** $z^2 + 4z + 20 = 0$
(iii) $9z^2 - 12z + 29 = 0$ **(iv)** $z^2 - 5jz - 6 = 0$

14 (i) Expand and simplify $(z - \alpha)(z - \beta)$. Deduce that the quadratic equation whose roots are α and β is $z^2 - (\alpha + \beta)z + \alpha\beta = 0$,
that is: $z^2 - (\text{sum of roots})z + (\text{product of roots}) = 0$.

(ii) Find quadratic equations in the form $az^2 + bz + c = 0$ whose roots are
(a) $7 + 4j, 7 - 4j$ **(b)** $\dfrac{5j}{3}, -\dfrac{5j}{3}$
(c) $-2 + \sqrt{8}j, -2 - \sqrt{8}j$ **(d)** $2 + j, 3 + 2j$

15 Find an example to show that *non-real* numbers p and q may be found such that the equation $z^2 + pz + q = 0$ has a real root. Is it possible for the equation to have two real roots if p and q are non-real?

16 Find real numbers a and b with $a > 0$ such that

(i) $(a + bj)^2 = 21 + 20j$ **(ii)** $(a + bj)^2 = -40 - 42j$

(iii) $(a + bj)^2 = 1 - 1.875j$ **(iv)** $(a + bj)^2 = j$

17 Given that $z = 2 + 3j$ is a solution of the equation

$$z^2 + (a - j)z + 16 + bj = 0$$

where a and b are real, find a, b and the other solution of the equation.

18 Write each expression as a product of linear factors with complex coefficients.

(i) $z^2 + 4$ **(ii)** $z^2 + 6z + 13$

(iii) $z^2 + z + 1$ **(iv)** $z^3 + 1$

19 (i) Evaluate **(a)** $(1 + j)^2$, **(b)** $(1 + j)^4$, and **(c)** $(1 + j)^{4k}$, where k is a positive integer.

(ii) By considering the binomial expansion of $(1 + j)^{4k}$, prove that

$$^{4k}C_0 - {}^{4k}C_2 + {}^{4k}C_4 - {}^{4k}C_6 + \ldots + {}^{4k}C_{4k} = (-4)^k.$$

(iii) Check this numerically in the cases **(a)** $k = 3$, **(b)** $k = 4$.

(iv) Investigate in a similar way the value of

$$^{4k+2}C_1 - {}^{4k+2}C_3 + {}^{4k+2}C_5 - {}^{4k+2}C_7 + \ldots + {}^{4k+2}C_{4k+1}.$$

Representing complex numbers geometrically

Since each complex number $x + yj$ corresponds uniquely to the ordered pair of real numbers (x, y), it is natural to represent $x + yj$ by the point with cartesian co-ordinates (x, y). For example, in figure 2.1,

$2 + 3j$ is represented by $(2, 3)$

$-5 - 4j$ is represented by $(-5, -4)$

$2j$ is represented by $(0, 2)$

7 is represented by $(7, 0)$

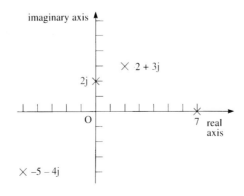

Figure 2.1

All real numbers are represented by points on the x axis, which is therefore called the *real axis*. Pure imaginary numbers (of the form $0 + y$j) give points on the y axis, which is called the *imaginary axis*. It is useful to label these Re and Im respectively. This geometrical interpretation of complex numbers is called the *complex plane* or the *Argand diagram* after Jean-Robert Argand (1768–1822), a self-taught Swiss book-keeper who published an account of it in 1806.

ACTIVITY

1 Copy figure 2.1. For each of the four given points z mark also the point $-z$. Describe the geometrical transformation which maps the point representing z to the point representing $-z$.

2 Describe the geometrical transformation which maps the point representing z to the point representing its complex conjugate z^*.

You will have seen in these activities that the points representing z and $-z$ have half-turn symmetry about the origin, and that the points representing z and z^* are reflections of each other in the real axis.

EXERCISE 2C

In Questions 1–6, represent the given complex numbers on an Argand diagram.

1 $3 + 2$j   2 4j   3 $-5 + $j

4 -2 5 $-6 - 5$j   6 $4 - 3$j

7 Given that $z = 2 - 4$j, represent the following by points on an Argand diagram.

(i) z (ii) $-z$ (iii) z^* (iv) $-z^*$

(v) $j z$ (vi) $-j z$ (vii) $j z^*$ (viii) $(j z)^*$

8 Given that $z = 10 + 5$j and $w = 1 + 2$j, show the following points on an Argand diagram.

(i) z (ii) w (iii) $z + w$ (iv) $z - w$

(v) $w - z$ (vi) $z w$ (vii) $\frac{z}{w}$ (viii) $\frac{w}{z}$

9 If $z = 1 + $j, plot the points z^n on a single Argand diagram for $n = -1, 0, 1, 2, 3, 4, 5$. Join each point to its predecessor and to the origin. What do you notice?

10 Give a geometrical proof that $(-z)^* = -z^*$.

Representing complex numbers by vectors

Several mathematicians before Argand had used the complex plane representation. In particular, a Norwegian surveyor, Caspar Wessel (1745–1818), wrote a paper in 1797 (largely ignored until it was republished in French a century later) in which the complex number $x + y$j is represented by the *position vector* $\binom{x}{y}$, see figure 2.2.

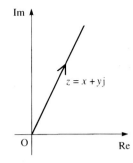

$z = x + yj$

Figure 2.2

The advantage of this is that the addition of complex numbers can then be shown by the addition of the corresponding vectors. This is because

$$z_1 + z_2 = (x_1 + x_2) + (y_1 + y_2)j \quad \text{and} \quad \begin{pmatrix} x_1 \\ y_1 \end{pmatrix} + \begin{pmatrix} x_2 \\ y_2 \end{pmatrix} = \begin{pmatrix} x_1 + x_2 \\ y_1 + y_2 \end{pmatrix}$$

so that the procedure of adding x and y components separately is the same in both cases (figure 2.3). In an Argand diagram the points representing $0, z_1, z_1 + z_2, z_2$ form a parallelogram (figure 2.4).

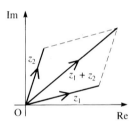

Figure 2.3

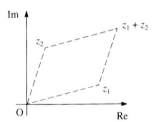

Figure 2.4

You can also represent z by any other directed line segment with components $\begin{pmatrix} x \\ y \end{pmatrix}$, not anchored at the origin as a position vector. Then addition can be shown by a triangle of vectors (see figure 2.5).

If you draw the other diagonal of the parallelogram, and let it represent the complex number w (figure 2.6) then

$$z_2 + w = z_1 \implies w = z_1 - z_2$$

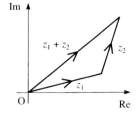

Figure 2.5

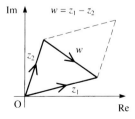

Figure 2.6

This gives a useful illustration of subtraction: the complex number $z_1 - z_2$ is represented by the vector from the point representing z_2 to the point representing z_1, as shown in figure 2.7.

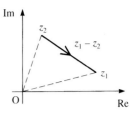

Figure 2.7

Note

1 In figure 2.7 notice:

    (a) the order of the points: the vector $z_1 - z_2$ goes *from* the point z_2 *to* the point z_1;

    (b) the simultaneous use of the point and vector representations.

2 From now on you can omit the words 'representing' or 'represented by', and just say, for example, 'the point 5 + 2j' or 'the vector 2 – 3j'.

ACTIVITY

1 Draw a diagram to illustrate $z_2 - z_1$.

2 Draw a diagram to illustrate that $z_1 - z_2 = z_1 + (-z_2)$. Show that this gives the same vector $z_1 - z_2$ as before, but represented by a line segment in a different place.

Having interpreted addition and subtraction in the Argand diagram you may wonder about multiplication and division. A few simple cases are explored in Questions 1 and 2 of Exercise 2D, but the full story is best left until a little later (page 34): it is worth waiting for!

EXERCISE 2D

1 (i) If $z = 2 + 3j$, plot the points kz on a single Argand diagram for
$$k = -2, -1, -\tfrac{1}{4}, 0, \tfrac{1}{2}, 1, 3.$$

    (ii) Repeat part **(i)** with a different z of your choice and a different set of real values of k.

    (iii) What is the relation between the points z and kz, where k is real?

2 (i) If $z = -4 + 2j$, represent the points z and jz by position vectors on a single diagram.

    (ii) Repeat part **(i)** for two other complex numbers z of your choice.

    (iii) What is the relation between the vectors z and jz?

    (iv) Explain how the geometrical interpretation of multiplication by j which you have given in part **(iii)** fits with the statement $j^2 = -1$.

    [**Hint:** Multiplying by j^2 means multiplying by j twice.]

3 The figure below consists of five squares on an Argand diagram. One vertex represents the number z, as shown. Copy the figure, and label each vertex with the complex number it represents.

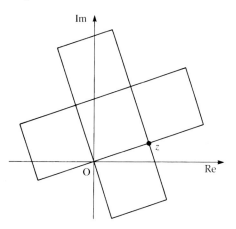

4 Prove that the point $\frac{1}{2}(z_1 + z_2)$ is halfway between the points z_1 and z_2.

5 In an Argand diagram the points A, B, C, D represent the complex numbers a, b, c, d respectively. Write down the vectors $\overrightarrow{AB}$ and $\overrightarrow{DC}$ in terms of a, b, c, d. Hence show that

$$\text{ABCD is a parallelogram} \iff a + c = b + d.$$

[**Note**: the term 'parallelogram' is here taken to include certain 'collapsed' cases, which you would not usually describe as parallelograms; you should identify these.]

6 If the points $2 - 3j$, $-1 - j$, $-3 + 4j$ are three vertices of a parallelogram, find all the possible fourth vertices. Draw all these parallelograms on a single Argand diagram.

7 The points $6 + j$, $-2 + 5j$ are the opposite vertices of a square.
   (i) Find the centre of the square and the vector from the centre to $6 + j$.
   (ii) Use Question 2 **(iii)** to find the other two vertices of the square.

8 Two vertices of a square are $7 + 2j$ and $3 - 6j$. Find the other vertices
   (i) when the given points are opposite vertices;
   (ii) when the given points are adjacent vertices, dealing with both possible squares.

The modulus of a complex number

The distance of the point representing z from the origin is called the *modulus* of z, and is denoted by $|z|$. Thus

$$z = x + y\text{j} \implies |z| = \sqrt{x^2 + y^2}.$$

If z is real, $z = x$ say, then $|z| = \sqrt{x^2}$, which is the absolute value of x, i.e. $|x|$. So the use of the modulus sign with complex numbers fits with its previous meaning for real numbers.

Sets of points in an Argand diagram

When z is represented by a vector, $|z|$ means the length of that vector. Since the vector $z_1 - z_2$ goes from the point z_2 to the point z_1 it follows that $|z_1 - z_2|$ is the distance between the points z_1 and z_2.

This is the key to solving many questions about sets of points in an Argand diagram, as in the following examples.

EXAMPLE 2.5

Draw an Argand diagram showing the set of points z for which $|z - 3 - 4\text{j}| = 5$.

SOLUTION

$|z - 3 - 4\text{j}|$ can be written as $|z - (3 + 4\text{j})|$, and this is the distance from the point $3 + 4\text{j}$ to the point z. This will equal 5 if and only if the point z lies on the circle with centre $3 + 4\text{j}$ and radius 5 (see figure 2.8).

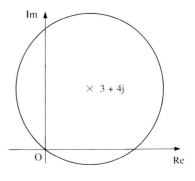

Figure 2.8

EXAMPLE 2.6

Draw an Argand diagram showing the set of points z for which $|z - 3 - 4\text{j}| \leqslant |z + 1 - 2\text{j}|$.

SOLUTION

$|z - 3 - 4\text{j}|$ is the distance from the point $3 + 4\text{j}$ (A say) to the point z as in the previous example, and $|z + 1 - 2\text{j}| = |z - (-1 + 2\text{j})|$ is the distance from the point $-1 + 2\text{j}$ (B say) to the point z. These distances are equal if and only if z is on the perpendicular bisector of AB. The given condition holds if and only if z is on this bisector or in the half plane on the side of it containing A (shaded in figure 2.9).

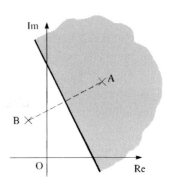

Figure 2.9

In Questions 1–7, draw an Argand diagram showing the set of points z for which the given condition is true.

1 $|z| = 2$

2 $|z - 4| \leqslant 3$

3 $|z - 5j| = 6$

4 $|z + 3 - 4j| < 5$

5 $|6 - j - z| \geqslant 2$

6 $|z + 2 + 4j| = 0$

7 $2 \leqslant |z - 1 + j| \leqslant 3$

8 Draw an Argand diagram showing the set of points z for which $|z - 12 + 5j| \leqslant 7$. Use the diagram to prove that, for these z, $6 \leqslant |z| \leqslant 20$.

9 What are the greatest and least values of $|z + 3 - 2j|$ if $|z - 5 + 4j| \leqslant 3$?

10 By using an Argand diagram see if it is possible to find values of z for which $|z - 2 + j| \geqslant 10$ and $|z + 4 + 2j| \leqslant 2$ simultaneously.

In Questions 11–18, draw an Argand diagram showing the set of points z for which the given condition is true.

11 $|z| = |z - 4|$

12 $|z| \geqslant |z - 2j|$

13 $\text{Re}(z) = -2$

14 $|z + 1 - j| = |z - 1 + j|$

15 $\text{Im}(z + 3 - 5j) < 0$

16 $|z + 5 + 7j| \leqslant |z - 2 - 6j|$

17 $|z + 8 + 2j| = |z - 6 + 2j| = |z - 4 - 4j|$

18 $|z + 8 + 2j| \leqslant |z - 6 + 2j| \leqslant |z - 4 - 4j|$

19 (i) Prove that if $|a| = |b|$ then the general point on the line through the point p perpendicular to the line joining points a and b can be written as $p + t(a + b)$, where t is real.

  (ii) ABCD is a cyclic quadrilateral. Through the mid-point of each side or diagonal a line is drawn perpendicular to the opposite side or other diagonal. Prove that these six lines meet at a single point.

Some properties of conjugates

First a reminder about notation. The conjugate of the complex number z is denoted by z^*, so that if $z = x + yj$ then $z^* = x - yj$, and the real and imaginary parts of z are denoted by $\text{Re}(z)$ and $\text{Im}(z)$ respectively.

Conjugates have the following properties.

1 $(z^*)^* = z$

2 $(z_1 + z_2)^* = z_1^* + z_2^*$

3 $(z_1 - z_2)^* = z_1^* - z_2^*$

4 $(z_1 z_2)^* = z_1^* z_2^*$

5 $\left(\dfrac{z_1}{z_2}\right)^* = \dfrac{z_1^*}{z_2^*}$

6 $\text{Re}(z) = \dfrac{z + z^*}{2}$, $\text{Im}(z) = \dfrac{z - z^*}{2j}$

All these properties can be proved directly from the definitions. For example, to prove **4**, let $z_1 = x_1 + y_1 j$ and $z_2 = x_2 + y_2 j$. Then

$$z_1 z_2 = (x_1 + y_1 j)(x_2 + y_2 j)$$
$$= (x_1 x_2 - y_1 y_2) + (x_1 y_2 + x_2 y_1)j$$
$$(z_1 z_2)^* = (x_1 x_2 - y_1 y_2) - (x_1 y_2 + x_2 y_1)j$$
$$= (x_1 - y_1 j)(x_2 - y_2 j)$$
$$= z_1^* z_2^*.$$

| ACTIVITY

Prove the other properties in a similar way.

Note

You may have found that to prove property **5** in this way is rather tedious; it is more elegant to make use of **4** to prove **5**, as follows.

Let $w = \dfrac{z_1}{z_2}$, so that $wz_2 = z_1$. Then $w^* z_2^* = z_1^*$ by **4**, so that $w^* = \dfrac{z_1^*}{z_2^*}$, which proves **5**.

| ACTIVITY

By putting $z_1 = z_2 = z$ in property **4** prove that $(z^2)^* = (z^*)^2$.
Then (putting $z_1 = z^2$, $z_2 = z$) prove that $(z^3)^* = (z^*)^3$.
Explain how to continue this process to prove that $(z^n)^* = (z^*)^n$.

There is a useful link between the conjugate and the modulus of a complex number: since $|z|^2 = x^2 + y^2 = (x + yj)(x - yj)$ it follows that $|z|^2 = zz^*$. This in turn leads to the further properties:

7 $|z_1 z_2| = |z_1||z_2|$

8 $\left|\dfrac{z_1}{z_2}\right| = \dfrac{|z_1|}{|z_2|}$

| ACTIVITY

Use properties of conjugates to prove properties **7** and **8**.

1 Given that $z = 2 + 3j$ and $w = 6 - 4j$, find

   (i) $\text{Re}(z)$ **(ii)** $\text{Im}(w)$ **(iii)** $z^* + w^*$ **(iv)** $\text{Im}(z + z^*)$

   (v) $(z^3)^*$ **(vi)** $(z^*)^3$ **(vii)** $zw^* - z^*w$

2 Given that $z = x + yj$ find $\dfrac{1}{z} + \dfrac{1}{z^*}$ in terms of x and y.

3 Prove that $\dfrac{1}{(\cos\theta + j\sin\theta)} = \cos\theta - j\sin\theta$.

4 (i) Use the properties of conjugates to prove that $z^n - (z^*)^n$ is pure imaginary (i.e. has zero real part).

  (ii) Simplify $(1 + j)^{-3} - (1 - j)^{-3}$.

5 (i) Simplify $(zw^*)^*$.

  (ii) Use conjugates to prove that $zw^* + z^*w$ is real and that $zw^* - z^*w$ is pure imaginary.

6 (i) Work out and simplify $(5 + 4j)^3$, and hence write down the simplified form of $(5 - 4j)^3$.

  (ii) Noting that $41 = 5^2 + 4^2 = (5 + 4j)(5 - 4j)$, use the result from part **(i)** to express 41^3 as the sum of two squares.

7 Find all the complex numbers z for which $z^2 = 2z^*$.

8 Use conjugates to prove that $|z - w|^2 + |z + w|^2 = 2|z|^2 + 2|w|^2$.

Deduce that the sum of the squares of the sides of a parallelogram equals the sum of the squares of its diagonals.

9 By representing z_1, z_2 and $z_1 + z_2$ as vectors, show that $|z_1 + z_2| \leqslant |z_1| + |z_2|$, and explain when equality occurs. Prove similarly that $|z_1 + z_2| \geqslant ||z_1| - |z_2||$. Verify these inequalities in the case $z_1 = 7 + 12j$, $z_2 = 5 + 7j$. (These are called the *triangle inequalities*.)

10 If $z = 12 - 9j$ and $|w| = 5$, find w

  (i) when $|z + w| = |z| + |w|$;

  (ii) when $|z + w| = |z| - |w|$.

11 Verify that $(c - a)(d - b) = (b - a)(d - c) + (d - a)(c - b)$. Use a triangle inequality to deduce that if A, B, C, D are any four points in a plane then

$$\text{AC} \times \text{BD} \leqslant \text{AB} \times \text{CD} + \text{AD} \times \text{BC}.$$

Complex numbers and equations

The reason for inventing complex numbers was to provide solutions for quadratic equations which have no real root, i.e. to solve $az^2 + bz + c = 0$ when the discriminant $b^2 - 4ac$ is negative. This is straightforward since if $b^2 - 4ac = -k^2$ (where k is real) then the formula for solving quadratic equations gives $z = \dfrac{-b \pm kj}{2a}$; these are the two complex roots of the equation. Notice that these roots are *conjugate* complex numbers.

It would be natural to think that to solve cubic equations would require a further extension of the number system to give some sort of 'super-complex' numbers, with ever more extensions to deal with higher degree equations. But luckily things are much simpler: it turns out that *all* polynomial equations (even those with complex coefficients) can be solved by means of complex numbers. This was realised as early as 1629 by Albert Girard, who stated that an nth degree polynomial equation has precisely n roots, including complex roots and taking into account repeated roots. (For example, the fifth degree equation $(z-2)(z-4)^2(z^2+9) = 0$ has the five roots 2, 4 (twice), 3j, −3j.) Many great mathematicians tried to prove this. The chief difficulty is to show that every polynomial equation must have at least *one* root: this is called the *Fundamental Theorem of Algebra*, and was first proved by Gauss (again!) in 1799.

The Fundamental Theorem (which is too difficult to prove here) is an example of an *existence theorem*: it tells us that a solution exists, but does not say what it is. To find the solutions of a particular equation you may be able to use an exact method such as the formula for the roots of a quadratic equation (there are much more complicated formulae for solving cubic or quartic equations, but not in general for equations of degree five or more). Alternatively, there are good approximate methods for finding roots to any required accuracy – you may have access to a computer or calculator with this facility.

| ACTIVITY

If so, find out how to use it.

You have already noted that the complex roots of a quadratic equation occur as a conjugate pair. The same is true of the complex roots of any polynomial equation with real coefficients. This can be proved by using the properties of conjugates you met in the previous section, as follows.

Let $P(z) = c_0 z^n + c_1 z^{n-1} + c_2 z^{n-2} + \ldots + c_n$ be a polynomial with *real* coefficients c_r. Then

$$
\begin{aligned}
(P(z))^* &= (c_0 z^n)^* + (c_1 z^{n-1})^* + (c_2 z^{n-2})^* + \ldots + c_n^* &&\text{(by property } \mathbf{2}\text{, page 26)}\\
&= c_0^*(z^n)^* + c_1^*(z^{n-1})^* + c_2^*(z^{n-2})^* + \ldots + c_n^* &&\text{(by property } \mathbf{4}\text{)}\\
&= c_0(z^n)^* + c_1(z^{n-1})^* + c_2(z^{n-2})^* + \ldots + c_n &&\text{(since the } c_r \text{ are real)}\\
&= c_0(z^*)^n + c_1(z^*)^{n-1} + c_2(z^*)^{n-2} + \ldots + c_n &&\text{(since } (z^r)^* = (z^*)^r\text{)}\\
&= P(z^*).
\end{aligned}
$$

Therefore

$$
\begin{aligned}
\alpha \text{ is a root of } P(z) = 0 \quad &\Leftrightarrow \quad P(\alpha) = 0\\
&\Leftrightarrow \quad P(\alpha^*) = (P(\alpha))^* = 0^* = 0\\
&\Leftrightarrow \quad \alpha^* \text{ is a root of } P(z) = 0.
\end{aligned}
$$

This shows that the complex roots of a polynomial equation with real coefficients occur in conjugate pairs: α is a root if and only if α^* is a root.

ACTIVITY

Show that the equation $z^2 - 3jz - 2 = 0$ has roots j and 2j, which are *not* conjugate. (This emphasises that the equation must have *real* coefficients for the theorem to hold.)

EXAMPLE 2.7

Given that $1 + 2j$ is a root of $4z^3 - 11z^2 + 26z - 15 = 0$, find the other roots.

SOLUTION

Since the coefficients are real, the conjugate $1 - 2j$ is also a root.
Therefore the polynomial $4z^3 - 11z^2 + 26z - 15$ has

$$[z - (1 + 2j)][z - (1 - 2j)] = [(z - 1) - 2j][(z - 1) + 2j]$$
$$= (z - 1)^2 + 4$$
$$= z^2 - 2z + 5 \text{ as a factor.}$$

By looking at the coefficient of z^3 and the constant term you can easily see that the remaining factor is $4z - 3$, and hence that the third root is $\frac{3}{4}$.

EXERCISE 2G

1 Check that $2 + j$ is a root of $z^3 - z^2 - 7z + 15 = 0$, and find the other roots.

2 One root of $z^3 - 15z^2 + 76z - 140 = 0$ is an integer. Solve the equation.

3 Given that $1 - j$ is a root of $z^3 + pz^2 + qz + 12 = 0$, find the real numbers p and q, and the other roots.

4 One root of $z^4 - 10z^3 + 42z^2 - 82z + 65 = 0$ is $3 + 2j$. Solve the equation.

5 The equation $z^4 - 8z^3 + 20z^2 - 72z + 99 = 0$ has a pure imaginary root. Solve the equation.

6 You are given the complex number $w = 1 - j$.
   (i) Express w^2, w^3 and w^4 in the form $a + bj$.
   (ii) Given that $w^4 + 3w^3 + pw^2 + qw + 8 = 0$, where p and q are real numbers, find the values of p and q.
   (iii) Write down two roots of the equation $z^4 + 3z^3 + pz^2 + qz + 8 = 0$, where p and q are the real numbers found in (ii).

   [MEI, part]

7 (i) Express $P(z) \equiv (z^2 + 25)(z^2 + 6z + 10)$ in the form $(z - \alpha)(z - \alpha^*)(z - \beta)(z - \beta^*)$.
   (ii) Find real polynomials $U(z)$ and $V(z)$ such that $(z - \alpha)(z - \beta) \equiv U(z) + jV(z)$, and write down $(z - \alpha^*)(z - \beta^*)$ in a similar form.
   (iii) Hence show that $P(z) \equiv [U(z)]^2 + [V(z)]^2$.

   [A *real* polynomial is a polynomial with real coefficients.]

8 Generalise the method of Question 7 to prove that any real polynomial $P(z)$ which is positive for all real values of z can be expressed as the sum of the squares of two real polynomials.

The polar form of complex numbers

The position vector of the point z in an Argand diagram can be described by means of its length r and the angle θ it makes with the positive real axis (figure 2.10).

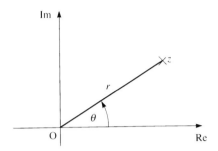

Figure 2.10

The distance r is of course $|z|$, the modulus of z as defined on page 24. The angle θ is slightly more complicated: it is measured anticlockwise from the positive real axis, normally in radians, but is not uniquely defined since adding $2k\pi$ (for any integer k) to θ gives the same direction. To avoid confusion, it is usual to choose that value of θ for which $-\pi < \theta \leqslant \pi$; this is called the *principal argument* of z, denoted by $\arg z$. Then every complex number except 0 has a unique principal argument: the argument of 0 is undefined. For example, with reference to figure 2.11,

$$\arg(-4) = \pi$$
$$\arg(-2\mathrm{j}) = -\frac{\pi}{2}$$
$$\arg(1.5) = 0$$
$$\arg(-3 + 3\mathrm{j}) = \frac{3\pi}{4}.$$

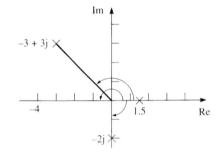

Figure 2.11

ACTIVITY

Find **(i)** $\arg \mathrm{j}$; **(ii)** $\arg(\sqrt{3} + \mathrm{j})$; **(iii)** $\arg(-4 - 4\mathrm{j})$; **(iv)** $\arg\left(\dfrac{-1 - \sqrt{3}\mathrm{j}}{2}\right)$.

It is clear from figure 2.12 that

$$x = r\cos\theta \qquad y = r\sin\theta$$
$$r = \sqrt{x^2 + y^2} \qquad \tan\theta = \frac{y}{x}$$

and the same relations hold in the other quadrants too.

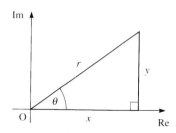

Figure 2.12

These can be used to find the real and imaginary parts from the modulus and argument, and vice versa, but care is needed in finding the argument from the real and imaginary parts. It is tempting to say that $\theta = \arctan\left(\frac{y}{x}\right)$, but this gives a value between $-\frac{\pi}{2}$ and $\frac{\pi}{2}$, which is correct only if z is in the first or fourth quadrants. For example, the point $z_1 = 2 - 3j$ is in the fourth quadrant, and its argument is correctly given by $\arctan\left(\frac{-3}{2}\right) \approx -0.98$ rad ($\approx -56°$). But $z_2 = -2 + 3j$ is in the second quadrant, where its argument is $\arctan\left(\frac{3}{-2}\right) + \pi \approx 2.16$ rad ($\approx 124°$) as in figure 2.13.

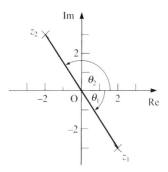

Figure 2.13

The general results for all quadrants are shown in figure 2.14. It is wise to draw a sketch diagram each time.

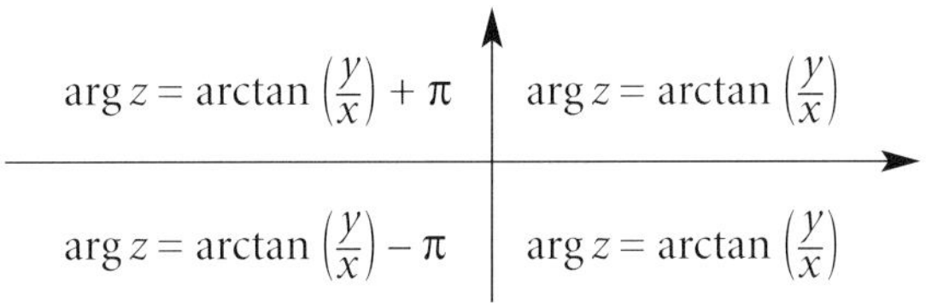

$$\arg z = \arctan\left(\frac{y}{x}\right) + \pi \quad \bigg| \quad \arg z = \arctan\left(\frac{y}{x}\right)$$

$$\arg z = \arctan\left(\frac{y}{x}\right) - \pi \quad \bigg| \quad \arg z = \arctan\left(\frac{y}{x}\right)$$

Figure 2.14

ACTIVITY

Mark the points $1 + j$, $1 - j$, $-1 + j$, $-1 - j$ on an Argand diagram. Find $\arg z$ for each of these, and check that the statements in figure 2.14 are correct.

ACTIVITY

Most calculators can convert from (x, y) to (r, θ) (called *rectangular* to *polar*, and often shown as R → P) and from (r, θ) to (x, y) (polar to rectangular, P → R). Find how to use these facilities on your calculator, and compare with other available types of calculator. Does your calculator always give the correct θ, or do you sometimes have to add or subtract π?

Since $x = r\cos\theta$ and $y = r\sin\theta$ we can write the complex number $z = x + yj$ in the form

$$z = r(\cos\theta + j\sin\theta).$$

This is called the *polar* or *modulus–argument* form. For example

$$-1 + j = \sqrt{2}\left(\cos\frac{3\pi}{4} + j\sin\frac{3\pi}{4}\right)$$

$$7j = 7\left(\cos\frac{\pi}{2} + j\sin\frac{\pi}{2}\right)$$

$$-3 = 3(\cos\pi + j\sin\pi)$$

$$4 + 3j = 5(\cos\alpha + j\sin\alpha) \text{ where } \alpha = \arctan\left(\frac{3}{4}\right) \approx 0.644.$$

In Questions 1–16, find the modulus and principal argument. Give the argument in radians, either as a simple rational multiple of π or correct to 3 decimal places.

1 1   **2** −2   **3** 3j   **4** −4j

5 1 + j   **6** −5 − 5j   **7** $1 - \sqrt{3}j$ **8** $6\sqrt{3} + 6j$

9 $-\sqrt{18} + \sqrt{18}j$

10 $8\left(\cos\frac{\pi}{5} + j\sin\frac{\pi}{5}\right)$

11 $\dfrac{\cos 2.3 + j\sin 2.3}{4}$

12 $-3(\cos(-3) + j\sin(-3))$

13 3 − 4j   **14** −12 + 5j   **15** 4 + 7j   **16** −58 − 93j

17 Given that $\arg(5 + 2j) = \alpha$, find the principal argument of each of the following in terms of α.

(i) −5 − 2j   **(ii)** 5 − 2j   **(iii)** −5 + 2j

(iv) 2 + 5j   **(v)** −2 + 5j

In Questions 18–22, write the complex numbers in polar form.

18 $\cos\alpha - j\sin\alpha$

19 $3(\sin\alpha + j\cos\alpha)$

20 $j(\cos\alpha + j\sin\alpha)$

21 $\dfrac{10}{\cos\alpha + j\sin\alpha}$

22 $1 + j\tan\alpha$

23 (i) Given that $z = \cos\theta + j\sin\theta$, plot the points 0, 1, z, 1 + z on an Argand diagram. What sort of quadrilateral do these points form? Hence find the modulus and argument of $1 + \cos\theta + j\sin\theta$.

(ii) Obtain the same result by expressing $1 + \cos\theta + j\sin\theta$ in terms of $\cos\frac{\theta}{2}$ and $\sin\frac{\theta}{2}$.

(iii) Find the modulus and argument of $1 - \cos\theta - j\sin\theta$.

24 (i) Given that $\alpha = -1 + 2j$, express α^2 and α^3 in the form $a + bj$. Hence show that α is a root of the cubic equation

$$z^3 + 7z^2 + 15z + 25 = 0.$$

(ii) Find the other two roots of this cubic equation.

(iii) Illustrate the three roots of the cubic equation on an Argand diagram, and find the modulus and argument of each root.

(iv) L is the locus of points in the Argand diagram representing complex numbers z for which $\left| z + \frac{5}{2} \right| = \frac{5}{2}$. Show that all three roots of the cubic equation lie on L and draw the locus L on your diagram.

[MEI]

Sets of points using the polar form

EXAMPLE 2.8

Draw Argand diagrams showing the sets of points z for which

(i) $\arg z = \dfrac{\pi}{4}$
(ii) $\arg(z - j) = \dfrac{\pi}{4}$
(iii) $0 \leqslant \arg(z - j) \leqslant \dfrac{\pi}{4}$
(iv) $\arg(z - j) = \arg(z - 2 + j)$

SOLUTION

(i) $\arg z = \dfrac{\pi}{4}$

$\Leftrightarrow$ the vector z has direction $\dfrac{\pi}{4}$

$\Leftrightarrow$ z lies on the half-line from the origin in the $\dfrac{\pi}{4}$ direction, see figure 2.15.

(Note that the origin is not included, since $\arg 0$ is undefined.)

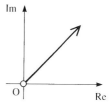

Figure 2.15

(ii) $\arg(z - j) = \dfrac{\pi}{4}$

$\Leftrightarrow$ the vector $z - j$ from the point j to the point z has direction $\dfrac{\pi}{4}$

$\Leftrightarrow$ z lies on the half-line from the point j in the $\dfrac{\pi}{4}$ direction, see figure 2.16.

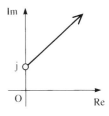

Figure 2.16

(iii) $0 \leqslant \arg(z - j) \leqslant \dfrac{\pi}{4}$

$\Leftrightarrow$ the vector $z - j$ from the point j to the point z has direction between 0 and $\dfrac{\pi}{4}$ (inclusive)

$\Leftrightarrow$ z lies in the one-eighth plane shown in figure 2.17.

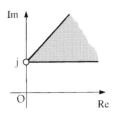

Figure 2.17

(iv) $\arg(z - \mathrm{j}) = \arg(z - 2 + \mathrm{j})$

⇔ the vectors from points j and $2 - \mathrm{j}$ to the point z are in the same direction and sense

⇔ z lies on the line joining points j and $2 - \mathrm{j}$, but does not lie between these points or at either of them, see figure 2.18.

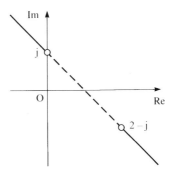

Figure 2.18

In Questions 1–6, *draw an Argand diagram showing the set of points z for which the given condition is true.*

1 $\arg z = -\dfrac{\pi}{3}$　　　　**2** $\arg(z - 4\mathrm{j}) = 0$　　　　**3** $\arg(z + 3) \geqslant \dfrac{\pi}{2}$

4 $\arg(z + 1 + 2\mathrm{j}) = \dfrac{3\pi}{4}$　　**5** $\arg(z - 3 + \mathrm{j}) \leqslant -\dfrac{\pi}{6}$　　**6** $-\dfrac{\pi}{4} \leqslant \arg(z + 5 - 3\mathrm{j}) \leqslant \dfrac{\pi}{3}$

7 Find the least and greatest possible values of $\arg z$ if $|z - 8\mathrm{j}| \leqslant 4$.

8 If k is positive and $|z| \leqslant k$, prove that $0 \leqslant |z + k| \leqslant 2k$ and $-\dfrac{\pi}{2} < \arg(z + k) < \dfrac{\pi}{2}$.

Find the least and greatest values of $|z + 2k|$ and $\arg(z + 2k)$.

In Questions 9–11, *draw an Argand diagram showing the set of points z for which the condition is true.*

9 $\arg z = \arg(z + 2)$

10 $\arg(z - 2 - 5\mathrm{j}) = \arg(z + 4 - 2\mathrm{j})$

11 $\arg(z + \mathrm{j}) = \arg(z - 3) + \pi.$

12 Prove that the set of points for which $\arg(z - 1) = \arg(z + 1) + \dfrac{\pi}{4}$ is part of the set of points for which $|z - \mathrm{j}| = \sqrt{2}$, and show which part clearly in a diagram.

Multiplication in the Argand diagram

The polar form quickly leads to an elegant geometrical interpretation of the multiplication of complex numbers. For if

$$z_1 = r_1(\cos\theta_1 + \mathrm{j}\sin\theta_1) \quad \text{and} \quad z_2 = r_2(\cos\theta_2 + \mathrm{j}\sin\theta_2)$$

then $z_1z_2 = r_1r_2(\cos\theta_1 + j\sin\theta_1)(\cos\theta_2 + j\sin\theta_2)$

$\qquad = r_1r_2[\cos\theta_1\cos\theta_2 - \sin\theta_1\sin\theta_2 + j(\sin\theta_1\cos\theta_2 + \cos\theta_1\sin\theta_2)].$

Using the compound angle formulae gives

$\qquad z_1z_2 = r_1r_2[\cos(\theta_1 + \theta_2) + j\sin(\theta_1 + \theta_2)].$

This is the complex number with modulus r_1r_2 and argument $(\theta_1 + \theta_2)$, so we have the beautiful result that

$\qquad |z_1z_2| = |z_1||z_2|$

and

$\qquad \arg(z_1z_2) = \arg z_1 + \arg z_2 \quad (\pm 2\pi$ if necessary, to give the principal argument).

So to multiply complex numbers in polar form you *multiply* their moduli and *add* their arguments.

| ACTIVITY

Using this interpretation, investigate **(i)** multiplication by j; **(ii)** multiplication by −1.

This gives the following simple geometrical interpretation of multiplication.

To obtain the vector z_1z_2, enlarge the vector z_1 by the scale factor $|z_2|$ and rotate it through $\arg z_2$ anticlockwise about O (figure 2.19).

This combination of an enlargement followed by a rotation is called a *spiral dilatation*.

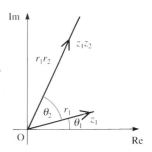

Figure 2.19

| ACTIVITY

Check this by accurate drawing and measurement for the case $z_1 = 2 + j$, $z_2 = 3 + 4j$. Then do the same with z_1 and z_2 interchanged.

The corresponding results for division are easily obtained by letting $\dfrac{z_1}{z_2} = w$. Then $z_1 = wz_2$ so that

$\qquad |z_1| = |w||z_2|$ and $\arg z_1 = \arg w + \arg z_2 \ (\pm 2\pi$ if necessary).

Therefore $|w| = \left|\dfrac{z_1}{z_2}\right| = \dfrac{|z_1|}{|z_2|}$

and $\qquad \arg w = \arg\dfrac{z_1}{z_2}$

$\qquad\qquad = \arg z_1 - \arg z_2 \ (\pm 2\pi$ if necessary, to give the principal argument).

So to divide complex numbers in polar form you *divide* their moduli and *subtract* their arguments.

In Questions 1–9, given that $z = 2\left(\cos\dfrac{\pi}{4} + j\sin\dfrac{\pi}{4}\right)$ *and*

$w = 3\left(\cos\dfrac{\pi}{3} + j\sin\dfrac{\pi}{3}\right)$, *find the following in polar form.*

1 wz **2** $\dfrac{w}{z}$ **3** $\dfrac{z}{w}$

4 $\dfrac{1}{z}$ **5** w^2 **6** z^5

7 w^3z^4 **8** $5jz$ **9** $(1+j)w$

10 Prove that, in general, $\arg\dfrac{1}{z} = -\arg z$, and deal with the exceptions.

11 Given the points 1 and z on an Argand diagram, explain how to find the following points by geometrical construction:

(i) $3z$ **(ii)** $2jz$ **(iii)** $(3+2j)z$

(iv) z^* **(v)** $|z|$ **(vi)** z^2

12 Describe the motion of each of the points in Question 11 as the point z moves

(a) along the imaginary axis from $-j$ to j;

(b) once anticlockwise around the circle $|z| = 1$, starting at $z = 1$.

13 By considering powers of $2+j$, show that the position vector $\binom{3}{4}$ bisects the angle formed by the position vectors $\binom{2}{1}$ and $\binom{2}{11}$. Check this by vector methods, using the scalar product.

14 Find the real and imaginary parts of $\dfrac{-1+j}{1+\sqrt{3}j}$.

Express $-1+j$ and $1+\sqrt{3}j$ in polar form.

Hence show that $\cos\dfrac{5\pi}{12} = \dfrac{\sqrt{3}-1}{2\sqrt{2}}$, and find an exact expression for $\sin\dfrac{5\pi}{12}$.

15 The complex numbers α and β are given by $\dfrac{\alpha+4}{\alpha} = 2-j$ and $\beta = -\sqrt{6}+\sqrt{2}j$.

(i) Show that $\alpha = 2+2j$.

(ii) Show that $|\alpha| = |\beta|$. Find $\arg\alpha$ and $\arg\beta$.

(iii) Find the modulus and argument of $\alpha\beta$. Illustrate the complex numbers α, β and $\alpha\beta$ on an Argand diagram.

(iv) Describe the locus of points in the Argand diagram representing complex numbers z for which $|z-\alpha| = |z-\beta|$. Draw this locus on your diagram.

(v) Show that $z = \alpha+\beta$ satisfies $|z-\alpha| = |z-\beta|$. Mark the point representing $\alpha+\beta$ on your diagram, and find the exact value of $\arg(\alpha+\beta)$.

[MEI]

16 The right-hand diagram below shows what happens to the character drawn on the Argand diagram on the left when each point representing z is replaced by the point representing z^2. Explain why

  (i)   the knife has moved nearer the origin, but got longer;

  (ii) his forearm has moved from vertical to horizontal;

  (iii) his boots have grown more than his head;

  (iv) he has stabbed himself in the stomach.

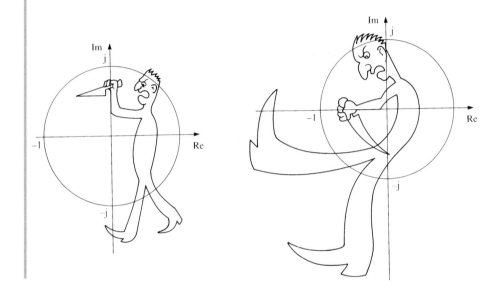

KEY POINTS

1 Complex numbers are of the form $z = x + y\mathrm{j}$ with $\mathrm{j}^2 = -1$.

2 The *conjugate* of z is $z^* = x - y\mathrm{j}$.

3 Addition and subtraction:

$$(x_1 + y_1\mathrm{j}) \pm (x_2 + y_2\mathrm{j}) = (x_1 \pm x_2) + (y_1 \pm y_2)\mathrm{j}$$

4 Multiplication:

$$(x_1 + y_1\mathrm{j})(x_2 + y_2\mathrm{j}) = (x_1 x_2 - y_1 y_2) + (x_1 y_2 + x_2 y_1)\mathrm{j}$$

5 Division – multiply top and bottom by the conjugate of the bottom:

$$\frac{x_1 + y_1\mathrm{j}}{x_2 + y_2\mathrm{j}} = \frac{(x_1 x_2 + y_1 y_2) + (x_2 y_1 - x_1 y_2)\mathrm{j}}{x_2^2 + y_2^2}$$

6 The complex number z can be represented geometrically as the point (x, y) [Argand] or the vector $\begin{pmatrix} x \\ y \end{pmatrix}$ [Wessel].

7 The modulus of $z = x + y\mathrm{j}$ is $|z| = \sqrt{x^2 + y^2}$; this is the distance of the point z from the origin, or the length of the vector z.

8 The distance between the points z_1 and z_2 in an Argand diagram is $|z_1 - z_2|$.

9 Modulus properties:

$$|z|^2 = zz^* \qquad |z_1 + z_2| \leqslant |z_1| + |z_2|$$

$$|z_1 z_2| = |z_1||z_2| \qquad \left|\frac{z_1}{z_2}\right| = \frac{|z_1|}{|z_2|}$$

10 The *principal argument* of z is the angle θ, $-\pi < \theta \leqslant \pi$, such that $\cos\theta : \sin\theta : 1 = x : y : r$, where $r = |z|$.

11 The *polar form* of z is $z = r(\cos\theta + \mathrm{j}\sin\theta)$.

12 Multiplication in polar form – multiply the moduli, add the arguments:

$$z_1 z_2 = r_1 r_2 \left[\cos(\theta_1 + \theta_2) + \mathrm{j}\sin(\theta_1 + \theta_2)\right]$$

13 Division in polar form – divide the moduli, subtract the arguments:

$$\frac{z_1}{z_2} = \frac{r_1}{r_2}\left[\cos(\theta_1 - \theta_2) + \mathrm{j}\sin(\theta_1 - \theta_2)\right]$$

3 Vector geometry

I pulled out, on the spot, a pocket book, which still exists, and made
an entry, on which, at the very moment, I felt it might be worth my
while to expend the labour of at least ten (or it might be fifteen) years
to come. But then it is fair to say that this was because I felt a
problem to have been at that moment solved, an intellectual want
relieved, which had haunted me for at least fifteen years before.

*William R Hamilton, writing on 16 October 1858 about his
invention of quaternions on 16 October 1843*

Multiplying vectors: the scalar product

In *Pure Mathematics 3* you met the scalar product $\mathbf{a.b}$ of two
vectors, $\mathbf{a}$ and $\mathbf{b}$:

$$\mathbf{a.b} = |\mathbf{a}||\mathbf{b}|\cos\theta$$

where θ is the angle between $\mathbf{a}$ and $\mathbf{b}$, the result being a scalar
(figure 3.1).

Figure 3.1

In two dimensions: $\quad \mathbf{a} = \begin{pmatrix} a_1 \\ a_2 \end{pmatrix} \quad \mathbf{b} = \begin{pmatrix} b_1 \\ b_2 \end{pmatrix} \quad \Rightarrow \quad \mathbf{a.b} = a_1 b_1 + a_2 b_2.$

In three dimensions: $\quad \mathbf{a} = \begin{pmatrix} a_1 \\ a_2 \\ a_3 \end{pmatrix} \quad \mathbf{b} = \begin{pmatrix} b_1 \\ b_2 \\ b_3 \end{pmatrix} \quad \Rightarrow \quad \mathbf{a.b} = a_1 b_1 + a_2 b_2 + a_3 b_3.$

Using the scalar product is an efficient way of finding the angle between two
vectors. It is particularly convenient if you want to test whether two vectors are
perpendicular, as then the scalar product is zero.

The scalar product also enables you to write down the equation of a plane: the
equation of a plane is $\mathbf{n.(r-a)} = 0$, where $\mathbf{a}$ is the position vector of the point A
on the plane, $\mathbf{r}$ is the position vector of a general point on the plane, and $\mathbf{n}$ is a
'normal', a vector perpendicular to the plane (see figure 3.2). This equation can
be rearranged as $\mathbf{n.r} = \mathbf{n.a}$, a scalar constant.

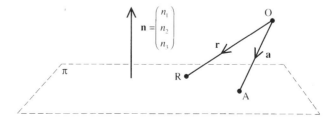

Figure 3.2

If $\mathbf{n} = \begin{pmatrix} n_1 \\ n_2 \\ n_3 \end{pmatrix}$ and $\mathbf{r} = \begin{pmatrix} x \\ y \\ z \end{pmatrix}$ the equation can be further rearranged as

$n_1 x + n_2 y + n_3 z + d = 0$, where d is a constant. (This is known as the cartesian form.)

Suppose, for example, an architect is designing a new roof with several triangular sections (figure 3.3). She decides she needs to find the cartesian equation of the plane containing the triangle with vertex A(3, 2, 10) and sloping edges given by the vectors $\begin{pmatrix} 8 \\ 1 \\ -4 \end{pmatrix}$ and $\begin{pmatrix} 7 \\ 4 \\ -4 \end{pmatrix}$. If she could easily find a normal $\mathbf{n}$ for the plane, finding the equation of the plane would only involve evaluating $\mathbf{n.a}$. The normal $\mathbf{n}$ is perpendicular to both $\begin{pmatrix} 8 \\ 1 \\ -4 \end{pmatrix}$ and $\begin{pmatrix} 7 \\ 4 \\ -4 \end{pmatrix}$ so the problem reduces to one of finding a vector perpendicular to two given vectors. One such vector is the vector product, which is now introduced.

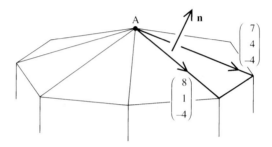

Figure 3.3

Multiplying vectors: the vector product

The *vector product* of $\mathbf{a}$ and $\mathbf{b}$ is a vector perpendicular to both $\mathbf{a}$ and $\mathbf{b}$; its magnitude is $|\mathbf{a}||\mathbf{b}|\sin\theta$, where θ is the angle between $\mathbf{a}$ and $\mathbf{b}$. The vector product of $\mathbf{a}$ and $\mathbf{b}$ is written as $\mathbf{a} \times \mathbf{b}$. Thus

$$\mathbf{a} \times \mathbf{b} = |\mathbf{a}||\mathbf{b}|\sin\theta\, \hat{\mathbf{n}}$$

where θ is the angle between $\mathbf{a}$ and $\mathbf{b}$, and $\hat{\mathbf{n}}$ is a unit vector which is perpendicular to both $\mathbf{a}$ and $\mathbf{b}$.

There are two unit vectors perpendicular to both $\mathbf{a}$ and $\mathbf{b}$, but they point in opposite directions; we sometimes say they have opposite *senses*. The vector $\hat{\mathbf{n}}$ is chosen such that $\mathbf{a}$, $\mathbf{b}$ and $\hat{\mathbf{n}}$ (in that order) form a right-handed set of vectors: if $\mathbf{a}$ and $\mathbf{b}$ are both horizontal, and if an anticlockwise rotation (between 0° and 180°) is needed to turn $\mathbf{a}$ to point in the same direction as $\mathbf{b}$, then $\mathbf{a} \times \mathbf{b}$ is the upwards vertical, as illustrated in figure 3.4. If you point the thumb of your right hand in the direction of $\mathbf{a}$, and your index finger in the direction of $\mathbf{b}$, then your second finger, coming 'up' from your palm, points in the direction of $\mathbf{a} \times \mathbf{b}$.

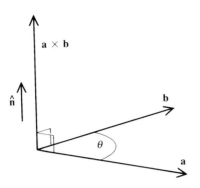
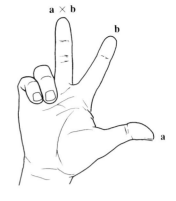

Figure 3.4

The following are important properties of vector products.

1 THE VECTOR PRODUCT IS ANTI-COMMUTATIVE

The vector products $\mathbf{a} \times \mathbf{b}$ and $\mathbf{b} \times \mathbf{a}$ have the same magnitude but are in opposite directions, so that $\mathbf{a} \times \mathbf{b} = -\mathbf{b} \times \mathbf{a}$. This is known as the *anti-commutative property*.

2 THE VECTOR PRODUCT OF PARALLEL VECTORS IS ZERO

This is because the angle θ between two parallel vectors is $0°$ or $180°$, so that $\sin\theta = 0$. Thus $\mathbf{a} \times \mathbf{a} = \mathbf{0}$ and in particular $\mathbf{i} \times \mathbf{i} = \mathbf{0}$.

Notice that $\mathbf{a} \times \mathbf{b}$ is also $\mathbf{0}$ if $\mathbf{a}$ or $\mathbf{b}$ is $\mathbf{0}$.

3 MULTIPLICATION BY SCALARS

If m is a scalar, the vector $m\mathbf{a}$ has magnitude $|m||\mathbf{a}|$; $m\mathbf{a}$ and $\mathbf{a}$ have the same direction if m is positive, but opposite directions if m is negative. Similar comments apply to $n\mathbf{b}$ and $\mathbf{b}$. Whatever the signs of m and n,

$$(m\mathbf{a}) \times (n\mathbf{b}) = mn(\mathbf{a} \times \mathbf{b}).$$

4 THE DISTRIBUTIVE PROPERTY OF VECTOR PRODUCT OVER VECTOR ADDITION

The property that $p(q + r) = pq + pr$, whatever the values of the numbers p, q and r, is known as the distributive property of multiplication over addition. It enables you to change a product into a sum of two simpler products – in doing so the multiplication is 'distributed' over the two terms of the original sum. Similarly, the process of forming a vector product is distributive over vector addition:

$$\mathbf{a} \times (\mathbf{b} + \mathbf{c}) = \mathbf{a} \times \mathbf{b} + \mathbf{a} \times \mathbf{c}.$$

This is clearly true for the trivial case of $\mathbf{a} = \mathbf{0}$, as then both sides simplify to $\mathbf{0}$, but we postpone the general proof to page 152.

The alternative form of the distributive property also holds, for

$$\mathbf{a} \times (\mathbf{b} + \mathbf{c}) = \mathbf{a} \times \mathbf{b} + \mathbf{a} \times \mathbf{c}$$
$$\Rightarrow \quad -\mathbf{a} \times (\mathbf{b} + \mathbf{c}) = -\mathbf{a} \times \mathbf{b} - \mathbf{a} \times \mathbf{c}$$
$$\Rightarrow \quad (\mathbf{b} + \mathbf{c}) \times \mathbf{a} = \mathbf{b} \times \mathbf{a} + \mathbf{c} \times \mathbf{a}$$

Multiplying by −1

By the anti-commutative property

5 THE VECTOR PRODUCT IN COMPONENT FORM

We shall shortly prove that if we express vectors $\mathbf{a}$ and $\mathbf{b}$ in terms of their components, so that $\mathbf{a} = a_1\mathbf{i} + a_2\mathbf{j} + a_3\mathbf{k}$ and $\mathbf{b} = b_1\mathbf{i} + b_2\mathbf{j} + b_3\mathbf{k}$, then

$$\mathbf{a} \times \mathbf{b} = \begin{pmatrix} a_1 \\ a_2 \\ a_3 \end{pmatrix} \times \begin{pmatrix} b_1 \\ b_2 \\ b_3 \end{pmatrix} = \begin{pmatrix} a_2 b_3 - a_3 b_2 \\ a_3 b_1 - a_1 b_3 \\ a_1 b_2 - a_2 b_1 \end{pmatrix}.$$

ACTIVITY

In this activity you may find it helpful to take the near edge of a rectangular table as the x axis, the left edge of the table as the y axis, and to hold a ruler pointing vertically upwards to represent the positive z axis, as in figure 3.5.

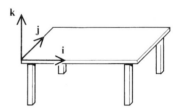

Figure 3.5

Use pens to represent:

$\mathbf{i}$, the unit vector pointing to the right along the x axis;
$\mathbf{j}$, the unit vector pointing away from you along the y axis;
$\mathbf{k}$, the unit vector pointing up along the z axis.

The vector product of $\mathbf{a}$ and $\mathbf{b}$ is defined as $\mathbf{a} \times \mathbf{b} = |\mathbf{a}||\mathbf{b}|\sin\theta\,\hat{\mathbf{n}}$, where θ is the angle between $\mathbf{a}$ and $\mathbf{b}$, and $\hat{\mathbf{n}}$ is a unit vector which is perpendicular to both $\mathbf{a}$ and $\mathbf{b}$, such that $\mathbf{a}, \mathbf{b}$ and $\hat{\mathbf{n}}$ (in that order) form a right-handed set of vectors.

Using the definition, check the truth of each of the following nine results:

$$\mathbf{i} \times \mathbf{i} = 0 \qquad \mathbf{i} \times \mathbf{j} = \mathbf{k} \qquad \mathbf{i} \times \mathbf{k} = -\mathbf{j}$$
$$\mathbf{j} \times \mathbf{i} = -\mathbf{k} \qquad \mathbf{j} \times \mathbf{j} = 0 \qquad \mathbf{j} \times \mathbf{k} = \mathbf{i}$$
$$\mathbf{k} \times \mathbf{i} = \mathbf{j} \qquad \mathbf{k} \times \mathbf{j} = -\mathbf{i} \qquad \mathbf{k} \times \mathbf{k} = 0.$$

(This is the first place in your work with vectors where it has been important that the positive x, y, z axes form a right-handed set.)

If $\mathbf{a} = a_1\mathbf{i} + a_2\mathbf{j} + a_3\mathbf{k}$ and $\mathbf{b} = b_1\mathbf{i} + b_2\mathbf{j} + b_3\mathbf{k}$, then

$$\begin{aligned}
\mathbf{a} \times \mathbf{b} &= (a_1\mathbf{i} + a_2\mathbf{j} + a_3\mathbf{k}) \times (b_1\mathbf{i} + b_2\mathbf{j} + b_3\mathbf{k}) \\
&= a_1b_1\mathbf{i} \times \mathbf{i} + a_1b_2\mathbf{i} \times \mathbf{j} + a_1b_3\mathbf{i} \times \mathbf{k} \\
&\quad + a_2b_1\mathbf{j} \times \mathbf{i} + a_2b_2\mathbf{j} \times \mathbf{j} + a_2b_3\mathbf{j} \times \mathbf{k} \\
&\quad + a_3b_1\mathbf{k} \times \mathbf{i} + a_3b_2\mathbf{k} \times \mathbf{j} + a_3b_3\mathbf{k} \times \mathbf{k} \\
&= \mathbf{0} + a_1b_2\mathbf{k} - a_1b_3\mathbf{j} - a_2b_1\mathbf{k} + \mathbf{0} + a_2b_3\mathbf{i} + a_3b_1\mathbf{j} - a_3b_2\mathbf{i} + \mathbf{0} \\
&= (a_2b_3 - a_3b_2)\mathbf{i} + (a_3b_1 - a_1b_3)\mathbf{j} + (a_1b_2 - a_2b_1)\mathbf{k}
\end{aligned}$$

Using properties 3 and 4 several times

Since $\mathbf{i} \times \mathbf{i} = 0$, $\mathbf{i} \times \mathbf{j} = \mathbf{k}$, $\mathbf{i} \times \mathbf{k} = -\mathbf{j}$, etc.

Thus $\mathbf{a} \times \mathbf{b} = \begin{pmatrix} a_1 \\ a_2 \\ a_3 \end{pmatrix} \times \begin{pmatrix} b_1 \\ b_2 \\ b_3 \end{pmatrix} = \begin{pmatrix} a_2b_3 - a_3b_2 \\ a_3b_1 - a_1b_3 \\ a_1b_2 - a_2b_1 \end{pmatrix}$.

The first component of $\mathbf{a} \times \mathbf{b}$ is the value of the 2×2 determinant $\begin{vmatrix} a_2 & b_2 \\ a_3 & b_3 \end{vmatrix}$ (see page 94) obtained by covering up the top row of $\begin{pmatrix} a_1 \\ a_2 \\ a_3 \end{pmatrix} \times \begin{pmatrix} b_1 \\ b_2 \\ b_3 \end{pmatrix}$; the second component is the negative of the 2×2 determinant obtained by covering up the middle row (note the sign); and the third component is the 2×2 determinant obtained by covering up the bottom row. You can therefore write

$$\mathbf{a} \times \mathbf{b} = \begin{pmatrix} a_1 \\ a_2 \\ a_3 \end{pmatrix} \times \begin{pmatrix} b_1 \\ b_2 \\ b_3 \end{pmatrix} = \begin{vmatrix} a_2 & b_2 \\ a_3 & b_3 \end{vmatrix}\mathbf{i} - \begin{vmatrix} a_1 & b_1 \\ a_3 & b_3 \end{vmatrix}\mathbf{j} + \begin{vmatrix} a_1 & b_1 \\ a_2 & b_2 \end{vmatrix}\mathbf{k}.$$

Note this sign

EXAMPLE 3.1

Calculate $\mathbf{a} \times \mathbf{b}$ when $\mathbf{a} = 3\mathbf{i} + 2\mathbf{j} + 5\mathbf{k}$ and $\mathbf{b} = \mathbf{i} - 4\mathbf{j} + 2\mathbf{k}$.

SOLUTION 1

$$\mathbf{a} \times \mathbf{b} = \begin{pmatrix} 3 \\ 2 \\ 5 \end{pmatrix} \times \begin{pmatrix} 1 \\ -4 \\ 2 \end{pmatrix} = \begin{pmatrix} 2 \times 2 - 5 \times (-4) \\ 5 \times 1 - 3 \times 2 \\ 3 \times (-4) - 2 \times 1 \end{pmatrix} = \begin{pmatrix} 24 \\ -1 \\ -14 \end{pmatrix}.$$

SOLUTION 2

$$\mathbf{a} \times \mathbf{b} = \begin{pmatrix} 3 \\ 2 \\ 5 \end{pmatrix} \times \begin{pmatrix} 1 \\ -4 \\ 2 \end{pmatrix} = \begin{pmatrix} 24 \\ -1 \\ -14 \end{pmatrix}$$

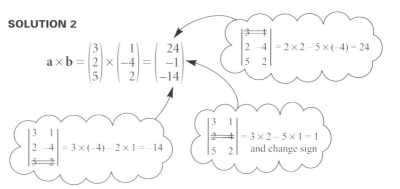

$\begin{vmatrix} 3 & 1 \\ 2 & -4 \\ 5 & 2 \end{vmatrix} = 2 \times 2 - 5 \times (-4) = 24$

$\begin{vmatrix} 3 & 1 \\ 2 & -4 \\ 5 & 2 \end{vmatrix} = 3 \times 2 - 5 \times 1 = 1$ and change sign

$\begin{vmatrix} 3 & 1 \\ 2 & -4 \\ 5 & 2 \end{vmatrix} = 3 \times (-4) - 2 \times 1 = -14$

EXAMPLE 3.2

Find $\mathbf{n} = \begin{pmatrix} 8 \\ 1 \\ -4 \end{pmatrix} \times \begin{pmatrix} 7 \\ 4 \\ -4 \end{pmatrix}$ and hence find the equation of the plane which contains the

point A(3, 2, 10) and the vectors $\begin{pmatrix} 8 \\ 1 \\ -4 \end{pmatrix} \times \begin{pmatrix} 7 \\ 4 \\ -4 \end{pmatrix}$.

(This is the architect's problem posed on page 40).

SOLUTION

$$\mathbf{n} = \begin{pmatrix} 8 \\ 1 \\ -4 \end{pmatrix} \times \begin{pmatrix} 7 \\ 4 \\ -4 \end{pmatrix} = \begin{pmatrix} 1 \times (-4) - (-4) \times 4 \\ -(8 \times (-4) - (-4) \times 7) \\ 8 \times 4 - 1 \times 7 \end{pmatrix} = \begin{pmatrix} 12 \\ 4 \\ 25 \end{pmatrix}$$

The cartesian equation of the plane is $12x + 4y + 25z =$ constant. As (3, 2, 10) is on the plane, the constant is $12 \times 3 + 4 \times 2 + 25 \times 10 = 294$.

The equation of the plane is $12x + 4y + 25z = 294$.

ACTIVITY

Some calculators can handle vectors. If yours does, or if you have access to a computer algebra system that handles vectors, find out how to use it to calculate the vector product of two vectors.

Note

It is wise to check that your result is perpendicular to both **a** and **b**. This can be done by checking (perhaps mentally) that the scalar product of your result with both **a** and **b** is indeed zero.

  Is it possible to find the vector product of two two-dimensional vectors?

EXAMPLE 3.3

Find the cartesian equation of the plane which contains the points A(3, 4, 2), B(2, 0, 5), C(6, 7, 8).

SOLUTION

You need to find a vector which is perpendicular to AB and BC (and CA).

$$\overrightarrow{AB} = \begin{pmatrix} 2 \\ 0 \\ 5 \end{pmatrix} - \begin{pmatrix} 3 \\ 4 \\ 2 \end{pmatrix} = \begin{pmatrix} -1 \\ -4 \\ 3 \end{pmatrix} \qquad \overrightarrow{BC} = \begin{pmatrix} 6 \\ 7 \\ 8 \end{pmatrix} - \begin{pmatrix} 2 \\ 0 \\ 5 \end{pmatrix} = \begin{pmatrix} 4 \\ 7 \\ 3 \end{pmatrix}$$

$$\Rightarrow \overrightarrow{AB} \times \overrightarrow{BC} = \begin{pmatrix} -1 \\ -4 \\ 3 \end{pmatrix} \times \begin{pmatrix} 4 \\ 7 \\ 3 \end{pmatrix} = \begin{pmatrix} -33 \\ 15 \\ 9 \end{pmatrix} = -3 \begin{pmatrix} 11 \\ -5 \\ -3 \end{pmatrix}$$

so $\mathbf{n} = \begin{pmatrix} 11 \\ -5 \\ -3 \end{pmatrix}$ is a vector perpendicular to plane ABC.

> Mentally check that $\mathbf{n}.\overrightarrow{AB} = \mathbf{n}.\overrightarrow{BC} = 0$

Plane ABC has equation $11x - 5y - 3z =$ constant. You can find the value of the constant by substituting the co-ordinates of A or B or C, obtaining 7.

The cartesian equation of plane ABC is $11x - 5y - 3z = 7$.

Note how it was helpful to remove common factors from the components of $\overrightarrow{AB} \times \overrightarrow{BC}$ so as to produce the simplest possible equation.

Finally here is an example where we are not expressing the vectors in terms of their components.

EXAMPLE 3.4

Simplify $(\mathbf{a} - \mathbf{b}) \times (\mathbf{a} + \mathbf{b})$.

> Distributive property applied twice. Notice the importance of keeping factors in their correct order

SOLUTION

$(\mathbf{a} - \mathbf{b}) \times (\mathbf{a} + \mathbf{b}) = \mathbf{a} \times \mathbf{a} + \mathbf{a} \times \mathbf{b} - \mathbf{b} \times \mathbf{a} - \mathbf{b} \times \mathbf{b}$

$= \mathbf{0} + \mathbf{a} \times \mathbf{b} - \mathbf{b} \times \mathbf{a} - \mathbf{0}$

> Vector product of parallel vectors is $\mathbf{0}$

$= \mathbf{a} \times \mathbf{b} + \mathbf{a} \times \mathbf{b}$

$= 2\mathbf{a} \times \mathbf{b}$

> Anti-commutative property

Historical note

The Irish mathematician William Rowan Hamilton (1805–1865) was appointed Professor of Astronomy at Trinity College, Dublin, at the age of 21, a post he held till the year of his death. Hamilton set out to create an algebra which was related to the rotation of three-dimensional space in much the same way that the algebra of complex numbers is related to the rotation of the plane. He defined a 'quaternion' as the sum of a real number and a 'triplet', a triplet being what we call a vector. For many years he was hampered because he expected to preserve the commutative property of multiplication; this turned out to be impossible in an algebra of three-dimensional rotations, and he finally defined multiplication in such a way that $\mathbf{a} \times \mathbf{b} = -\mathbf{b} \times \mathbf{a}$, though it appears that Carl Friedrich Gauss (1777–1855) had reached similar results about 30 years previously. Also in Germany, Hermann Günther Grassmann (1809–1877) independently developed similar ideas. Quaternions did not long survive Hamilton, but vectors became a major tool for physicists, though not all considered them useful. Even the eminent Lord Kelvin (1824–1907) wrote: 'Vector is a useless survival or off-shoot from quaternion and has never been of the slightest use to any creature.'

EXERCISE 3A

1 Calculate each of the following vector products.

(i) $\begin{pmatrix} 3 \\ 5 \\ 2 \end{pmatrix} \times \begin{pmatrix} 2 \\ 4 \\ -3 \end{pmatrix}$

(ii) $\begin{pmatrix} 7 \\ -4 \\ -5 \end{pmatrix} \times \begin{pmatrix} -4 \\ 5 \\ -3 \end{pmatrix}$

(iii) $\begin{pmatrix} 5 \\ -2 \\ 4 \end{pmatrix} \times \begin{pmatrix} 1 \\ 5 \\ -6 \end{pmatrix}$

(iv) $(3\mathbf{i} - 7\mathbf{k}) \times (2\mathbf{i} + 3\mathbf{j} + 5\mathbf{k})$

2 The distributive property of vector product over vector addition states that

$$\mathbf{a} \times (\mathbf{b} + \mathbf{c}) = \mathbf{a} \times \mathbf{b} + \mathbf{a} \times \mathbf{c} \quad \text{and} \quad (\mathbf{a} + \mathbf{b}) \times \mathbf{c} = \mathbf{a} \times \mathbf{c} + \mathbf{b} \times \mathbf{c}.$$

Check that these are both true when

$$\mathbf{a} = 3\mathbf{i} + 4\mathbf{j} + 6\mathbf{k} \quad \mathbf{b} = 8\mathbf{i} + 2\mathbf{j} + 5\mathbf{k} \quad \mathbf{c} = 7\mathbf{i} - 3\mathbf{j} + 9\mathbf{k}.$$

3 Find vectors perpendicular to the following pairs of vectors:

(i) $\begin{pmatrix} 2 \\ 0 \\ 5 \end{pmatrix}, \begin{pmatrix} 3 \\ -1 \\ -2 \end{pmatrix}$ 　　　 (ii) $\begin{pmatrix} 12 \\ 3 \\ -2 \end{pmatrix}, \begin{pmatrix} 7 \\ 1 \\ 4 \end{pmatrix}$

(iii) $\begin{pmatrix} 2 \\ 3 \\ 4 \end{pmatrix}, \begin{pmatrix} 3 \\ 6 \\ 7 \end{pmatrix}$ 　　　 (iv) $\begin{pmatrix} 3 \\ -4 \\ 6 \end{pmatrix}, \begin{pmatrix} 8 \\ 5 \\ -3 \end{pmatrix}$

4 Find a unit vector perpendicular to both $\mathbf{i} + 2\mathbf{j} + 7\mathbf{k}$ and $3\mathbf{i} - \mathbf{j} + 6\mathbf{k}$.

5 Find the cartesian equations of the planes containing the three points

(i) M(1, 4, 2), E(5, 1, 3), I(1, 0, 0)

(ii) T(5, −3, 4), J(0, 1, 0), H(6, 2, 5)

(iii) D(6, 2, −2), R(1, 4, 3), M(−5, 7, 1)

(iv) C(4, 2, −1), L(8, 2, 4), S(5, 8, −7)

6 The angle between $\mathbf{p} = \begin{pmatrix} 5 \\ -3 \\ 1 \end{pmatrix}$ and $\mathbf{q} = \begin{pmatrix} -2 \\ -5 \\ 2 \end{pmatrix}$ is θ.

(i) Calculate $\mathbf{p} \times \mathbf{q}$ and $|\mathbf{p} \times \mathbf{q}|$ and hence find the value of $\sin\theta$.

(ii) Calculate $\mathbf{p.q}$ and hence find the value of $\cos\theta$.

(iii) Show that the results you obtained in (i) and (ii) fit the identity

$$\sin^2\theta + \cos^2\theta \equiv 1.$$

(iv) If you want to find the angle between two vectors it is usually quicker to use the scalar product rather than the vector product. Give another reason why the scalar product method is preferable.

7 What can you say about $\mathbf{a}$ and $\mathbf{b}$ if $\mathbf{a} \times \mathbf{c} = \mathbf{b} \times \mathbf{c}$?

8 Explain why $\mathbf{a}.(\mathbf{a} \times \mathbf{b}) = 0$.

9 $\mathbf{v}$ and $\mathbf{w}$ are non-parallel vectors.

Show that $(\mathbf{v} + 2\mathbf{w}) \times (\mathbf{v} - 3\mathbf{w}) = k(\mathbf{v} \times \mathbf{w})$, where the real number k is to be found.

[MEI, part]

10 In triangle ABC, let $\overrightarrow{BC}$, $\overrightarrow{CA}$, and $\overrightarrow{AB}$ be denoted by $\mathbf{a}$, $\mathbf{b}$, and $\mathbf{c}$, as illustrated. Show that $\mathbf{a} \times \mathbf{b} = \mathbf{b} \times \mathbf{c} = \mathbf{c} \times \mathbf{a}$, and use this result to complete an alternative proof of the sine rule.

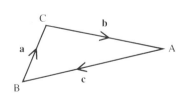

11 The moment of a force **F** about the origin O is
r × **F**, where **r** is the position vector of any point R
on the line of action of **F**. Prove that the moment of
a force about O is independent of the choice of
the point R, provided R is on the line of action of **F**.

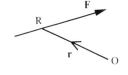

12 If a body is rotating at angular speed ω about an axis through O (see below)
then the angular velocity is represented by the vector **ω**, defined to have
magnitude ω and be parallel to the axis such that a right-handed corkscrew
attached to the body would move in the direction indicated by **ω**.

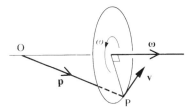

Show that the velocity **v** of a point P on the rotating body is given by
v = **ω** × **p**, where **p** is the position vector of P.

The intersection of two planes

If you look around you will find objects which can be used to represent planes –
walls, floors, ceilings, doors, roofs, and so on. You will see that the intersection of
two planes is a straight line.

EXAMPLE 3.5

Find *l*, the line of intersection of the two planes

$$3x + 2y - 3z = -18 \quad \text{and} \quad x - 2y + z = 12.$$

SOLUTION 1

This solution depends on finding two points on *l*.

You can find one point by arbitrarily choosing to put
$y = 0$ into the equations of the planes and solving
simultaneously:

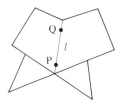

Figure 3.6

$$\left.\begin{matrix} 3x - 3z = -18 \\ x + y = 12 \end{matrix}\right\} \Leftrightarrow \left\{\begin{matrix} x - z = -6 \\ x + z = 12 \end{matrix}\right\} \Leftrightarrow x = 3, z = 9.$$

So P with co-ordinates (3, 0, 9) is a point on *l*.

(You could run into difficulties putting $y = 0$ as it is possible that the line has no
points where $y = 0$. In this case your simultaneous equations for x and z would
be inconsistent; you would then choose a value for x or z instead.)

Choosing to put $z = 1$ into the equations gives

$$\left.\begin{array}{r} 3x + 2y = -15 \\ x - 2y = 11 \end{array}\right\} \Leftrightarrow \left.\begin{array}{r} 4x = -4 \\ 2y = x - 11 \end{array}\right\} \Leftrightarrow x = -1, y = -6$$

so Q with co-ordinates $(-1, -6, 1)$ is a point on l.

$$\overrightarrow{PQ} = \begin{pmatrix} -1 \\ -6 \\ 1 \end{pmatrix} - \begin{pmatrix} 3 \\ 0 \\ 9 \end{pmatrix} = \begin{pmatrix} -4 \\ -6 \\ -8 \end{pmatrix} = -2\begin{pmatrix} 2 \\ 3 \\ 4 \end{pmatrix}$$

> Removing factor -2 makes the arithmetic simpler

Use $\begin{pmatrix} 2 \\ 3 \\ 4 \end{pmatrix}$ as the direction vector for l.

A vector equation for l is $\mathbf{r} = \begin{pmatrix} -1 \\ -6 \\ 1 \end{pmatrix} + t\begin{pmatrix} 2 \\ 3 \\ 4 \end{pmatrix}$.

You can give the cartesian form of the equations: $\dfrac{x + 1}{2} = \dfrac{y + 6}{3} = \dfrac{z - 1}{4}$

or the parametric form: $\begin{cases} x = 2t - 1 \\ y = 3t - 6 \\ z = 4t + 1 \end{cases}$.

SOLUTION 2

The planes have normals $\mathbf{n}_1 = \begin{pmatrix} 3 \\ 2 \\ -3 \end{pmatrix}$ and $\mathbf{n}_2 = \begin{pmatrix} 1 \\ -2 \\ 1 \end{pmatrix}$.

As line l is in each plane (see figure 3.7) it must be perpendicular to both $\mathbf{n}_1$ and $\mathbf{n}_2$, so

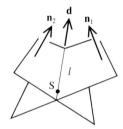

Figure 3.7

$$\mathbf{n}_1 \times \mathbf{n}_2 = \begin{pmatrix} -4 \\ -6 \\ -8 \end{pmatrix} = -2\begin{pmatrix} 2 \\ 3 \\ 4 \end{pmatrix}$$

> Removing factor -2 makes the arithmetic simpler

gives a vector in the direction of l.

Use $\mathbf{d} = \begin{pmatrix} 2 \\ 3 \\ 4 \end{pmatrix}$ as the direction vector for l.

> Mentally check that $\mathbf{d.n}_1 = \mathbf{d.n}_2 = 0$

Now you only need to find a point S on l.

Choosing to put $x = 1$ into the equations gives

$$\left.\begin{array}{r} 2y - 3z = -21 \\ -2y + z = 11 \end{array}\right\} \Leftrightarrow \left.\begin{array}{r} -2z = -10 \\ 2y = 3z - 21 \end{array}\right\} \Leftrightarrow z = 5, y = -3$$

so S with co-ordinates $(1, -3, 5)$ is a point on line l.

The cartesian equations of l are $\dfrac{x - 1}{2} = \dfrac{y + 3}{3} = \dfrac{z - 5}{4}$, though you could give

the parametric form $\begin{cases} x = 2t + 1 \\ y = 3t - 3 \\ z = 4t + 5 \end{cases}$ or the vector form $\mathbf{r} = \begin{pmatrix} 1 \\ -3 \\ 5 \end{pmatrix} + t\begin{pmatrix} 2 \\ 3 \\ 4 \end{pmatrix}$.

Note

These equations do not look the same as the previous equations because S(1, –3, 5) was used instead of Q(–1, –6, 1) as the 'starting point' for the line. There are infinitely many 'starting points' available. Putting $x = -1$ in the equations obtained at the end of Solution 2 gives $t = -1$, $y = -6$, $z = 1$, showing that the line does go through the point Q(–1, –6, 1): these two solutions are equivalent as they have a common point and the same direction vector.

SOLUTION 3

In this solution the original two equations in x, y and z are solved, expressing each of x, y and z in terms of some parameter.

Put $x = \lambda$ into $\begin{cases} 3x + 2y - 3z = -18 \\ x - 2y + z = 12 \end{cases}$ and solve simultaneously for y and z:

$$\left.\begin{cases} 2y - 3z = -18 - 3\lambda \\ -2y + z = 12 - \lambda \end{cases}\right\} \Rightarrow -2z = -6 - 4\lambda \Rightarrow z = 2\lambda + 3.$$

so that $2y = 3z - 18 - 3\lambda = 3(2\lambda + 3) - 18 - 3\lambda = 3\lambda - 9$ and $y = \frac{3}{2}\lambda - \frac{9}{2}$.

Thus the parametric equations for l are

$$\begin{cases} x = \lambda \\ y = \frac{3}{2}\lambda - \frac{9}{2} \\ z = 2\lambda + 3 \end{cases} \quad \text{or} \quad \begin{pmatrix} x \\ y \\ z \end{pmatrix} = \begin{pmatrix} 0 \\ -\frac{9}{2} \\ 3 \end{pmatrix} + \lambda \begin{pmatrix} 1 \\ \frac{3}{2} \\ 2 \end{pmatrix}.$$

Note

Again this set of equations is different from but equivalent to the earlier equations. The equivalence is most easily seen by substituting $2\mu - 1$ for λ, obtaining

$$\begin{cases} x = 2\mu - 1 \\ y = \frac{3}{2}(2\mu - 1) - \frac{9}{2} = 3\mu - 6 \\ z = 2(2\mu - 1) + 3 = 4\mu + 1 \end{cases}$$

Notice that cartesian equations of a line, such as $\dfrac{x-1}{5} = \dfrac{y-3}{7} = \dfrac{z-4}{2}$, are equivalent to the pair of equations

$$\frac{x-1}{5} = \frac{y-3}{7} \quad \text{and} \quad \frac{y-3}{7} = \frac{z-4}{2}.$$

These can be rearranged as $\begin{cases} 7x - 5y = -8 \\ 2y - 7z = -22 \end{cases}$ which are the equations of planes.

You can always convert the cartesian equations of a line into the equations of two planes. Every straight line may be regarded as the intersection of two planes.

Angle between two planes

The angle between two planes can be found by using the scalar product. As figures 3.8 and 3.9 make clear, the angle between planes π_1 and π_2 is the same as the angle between their normals, $\mathbf{n}_1$ and $\mathbf{n}_2$.

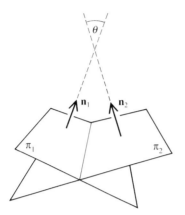

Figure 3.8

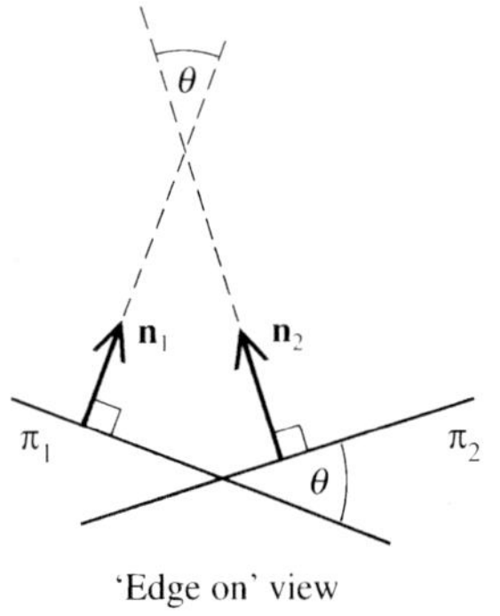

'Edge on' view

Figure 3.9

EXAMPLE 3.6

Find the acute angle between the planes π_1: $2x + 3y + 5z = 8$ and π_2: $5x + y - 4z = 12$.

SOLUTION

The planes have normals $\mathbf{n}_1 = \begin{pmatrix} 2 \\ 3 \\ 5 \end{pmatrix}$ and $\mathbf{n}_2 = \begin{pmatrix} 5 \\ 1 \\ -4 \end{pmatrix}$, so $\mathbf{n}_1.\mathbf{n}_2 = 10 + 3 - 20 = -7$.

The angle between the normals is θ, where

$$\cos\theta = \frac{\mathbf{n}_1.\mathbf{n}_2}{|\mathbf{n}_1||\mathbf{n}_2|} = \frac{-7}{\sqrt{38}\sqrt{42}} \Rightarrow \theta \approx 100°.$$

Therefore the acute angle between the planes is about 80°.

Sheaf of planes

When several planes share a common line the arrangement is known as a *sheaf of planes* (figure 3.10). The next example shows how you can find the equation of a plane which contains the line *l* common to two given planes, π_1 and π_2, without having to find the equation of *l* itself, or any points on *l*.

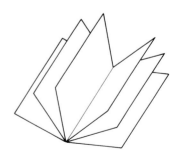

Figure 3.10

EXAMPLE 3.7

Find the equation of the plane which passes through the point $(1, 2, 3)$ and contains the common line of the planes $\pi_1: 2x + 2y + z + 3 = 0$ and $\pi_2: 2x + 3y + z + 13 = 0$.

SOLUTION

The equation

$$p(2x + 2y + z + 3) + q(2x + 3y + z + 13) = 0 \qquad \text{①}$$

can be rearranged in the form $ax + by + cz + d = 0$, where not all of a, b, c, d are zero provided p and q are not both zero. Therefore equation ① represents a plane. Further, any point (x, y, z) which satisfies both π_1 and π_2 will also satisfy equation ①. Thus equation ① represents a plane containing the common line of planes π_1 and π_2. Substituting $(1, 2, 3)$ into ① gives

$$12p + 24q = 0 \quad \Leftrightarrow \quad p = -2q.$$

The required equation is

$$-2q(2x + 2y + z + 3) + q(2x + 3y + z + 13) = 0$$
$$\Leftrightarrow \qquad\qquad\qquad\qquad -q(2x + y + z - 7) = 0$$

so that the required plane has equation $2x + y + z - 7 = 0$.

? Planes π_1 and π_2 have equations $a_1x + b_1y + c_1z + d_1 = 0$ and $a_2x + b_2y + c_2z + d_2 = 0$ respectively. Plane π_3 has equation

$$p(a_1x + b_1y + c_1z + d_1) + q(a_2x + b_2y + c_2z + d_2) = 0.$$

How is π_3 related to π_1 and π_2 if π_1 and π_2 are parallel?

The following example illustrates one method of solving simultaneous equations in three unknowns. An alternative procedure is given in Chapter 5 (page 113).

EXAMPLE 3.8

Planes π_1: $9x + 3y - 5z = 12$
 π_2: $7x + 2y - 4z = 8$
 π_3: $13x + 4y - 7z = 18$

meet at the point P (see figure 3.11). Plane π_4 contains the common line of planes π_1 and π_3; π_5 contains the common line of π_2 and π_3; both π_4 and π_5 pass through the origin, O.

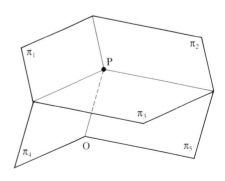

Figure 3.11

(i) Find the equations of planes π_4 and π_5.

(ii) Find a vector parallel to both planes π_4 and π_5.

(iii) Hence find the co-ordinates of P.

SOLUTION

(i) π_1: $9x + 3y - 5z = 12$ $\quad$ π_3: $13x + 4y - 7z = 18$

Find π_4 by adding multiples of π_1 and π_3.

As π_4 passes through the origin its 'constant term' is 0.

Eliminate the constant terms in π_1 and π_3 by calculating $3\pi_1 - 2\pi_3$,

getting	π_4: $\quad x + y - z = 0$
Eliminating the constant terms in	π_2: $\quad 7x + 2y - 4z = 8$
and	π_3: $\quad 13x + 4y - 7z = 18$
by calculating $9\pi_2 - 4\pi_3$ gives	π_5: $\quad 11x + 2y - 8z = 0$.

(ii) Using $\mathbf{n}_4$ and $\mathbf{n}_5$ to represent the normals to π_4 and π_5, a vector parallel to both these planes will be

$$\mathbf{n}_4 \times \mathbf{n}_5 = \begin{pmatrix} 1 \\ 1 \\ -1 \end{pmatrix} \times \begin{pmatrix} 11 \\ 2 \\ -8 \end{pmatrix} = \begin{pmatrix} -6 \\ -3 \\ -9 \end{pmatrix} = -3\begin{pmatrix} 2 \\ 1 \\ 3 \end{pmatrix}.$$

(iii) The vector $\begin{pmatrix} 2 \\ 1 \\ 3 \end{pmatrix}$ is parallel to both π_4 and π_5, and is therefore parallel to their common line, OP, so that $\overrightarrow{OP} = \lambda\begin{pmatrix} 2 \\ 1 \\ 3 \end{pmatrix}$ for some λ, and P has co-ordinates $(2\lambda, \lambda, 3\lambda)$. Substituting these into the equation for π_3 you obtain

$$13(2\lambda) + 4\lambda - 7(3\lambda) = 18 \quad \Leftrightarrow \quad 9\lambda = 18$$

so that $\lambda = 2$, and P has co-ordinates $(4, 2, 6)$.

EXERCISE 3B

1 Find cartesian equations of the line of intersection of the pairs of planes

(i) $x + y - 6z = 4$, $5x - 2y - 3z = 13$

(ii) $5x - y + z = 8$, $x + 3y + z = -4$

(iii) $3x + 2y - 6z = 4$, $x + 5y - 7z = 2$

(iv) $5x + 2y - 3z = -2$, $3x - 3y - z = 2$

2 Find the acute angle between each pair of planes in Question 1.

3 Find cartesian equations of the line which passes through the given point and which is parallel to the line of intersection of the two planes

(i) $(-2, 3, 5)$, $4x - y + 3z = 5$, $3x - y + 2z = 7$

(ii) $(4, -3, 2)$, $2x + 3y + 2z = 6$, $4x - 3y + z = 11$

4 Find the equation of the plane which goes through $(3, 2, -2)$ and which contains the common line of $x + 7y - 2z - 3 = 0$ and $2x - 3y + 2z - 1 = 0$.

5 Find the equation of the plane which contains the point $(1, -2, 3)$ and which is perpendicular to the common line of $5x - 3y - 4z = 2$ and $2x + y + 5z = 7$.

6 Find the equation of the line which goes through $(4, -2, -7)$ and which is parallel to both $2x - 5y - 2z = 8$ and $x + 3y - 3z = 12$.

7 The diagram shows the co-ordinates of the corners of parts of the roof of a warehouse.

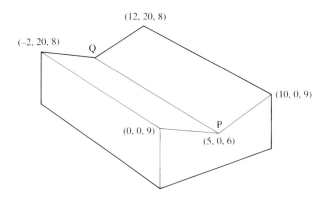

Find the equations of both roof sections, and the vector equation of the line PQ. Assuming that the z axis is vertical, what angle does PQ make with the horizontal?

8 Test drilling in the Namibian desert has shown the existence of gold deposits at $(400, 0, -400)$, $(-50, 500, -250)$, $(-200, -100, -200)$, where the units are in metres, the x axis points east, the y axis points north, and the z axis points up. Assume that these deposits are part of the same seam, contained in plane π.

  (i) Find the equation of plane π.

  (ii) Find the angle at which π is tilted to the horizontal.

The drilling positions $(400, 0, 3)$, $(-50, 500, 7)$, $(-200, -100, 5)$ are on the desert floor. Take the desert floor as a plane, Π.

  (iii) Find the equation of Π.

  (iv) Find the equation of the line where the plane containing the gold seam intersects the desert floor.

  (v) How far south of the origin does the line found in part **(iv)** pass?

9 Find the common point of the following sets of planes.

  (i) $x + 3y + 2z = -7$, $3x + 5y + 4z = -7$, $x + 2y + z = -5$

  (ii) $9x - 3y - z = -4$, $x - 3y + z = 12$, $7x - 4y - 3z = -7$

  (iii) $6x + 9y + 5z = 17$, $5x - 8y - z = 40$, $9x - 2y - 8z = 41$

10 What happens if you attempt to use the method shown in Example 3.8 to find the common point of the following planes?

$$x + 2y + z = 10 \qquad 2x - y + 3z = 20 \qquad 3x + y + 4z = 30$$

11 (i) Calculate the vector product $(4\mathbf{i} - 3\mathbf{j} - 4\mathbf{k}) \times (9\mathbf{i} + 7\mathbf{j} + 2\mathbf{k})$.

(ii) Find the equation of the line of intersection of the two planes

$$4x - 3y - 4z = 14$$
$$\text{and} \quad 9x + 7y + 2z = 4.$$

(iii) Find the values of a and d if the three planes

$$4x - 3y - 4z = 14$$
$$9x + 7y + 2z = 4$$
$$ax + 4y + 2z = d$$

intersect along a common line.

[MEI, part]

The intersection of lines

Hold a pen and a pencil to represent two distinct straight lines as follows:

- hold them to represent parallel lines;

- hold them to represent intersecting lines;

- hold them to represent lines which are not parallel and which do not intersect (even if you extend them).

In three-dimensional space two or more straight lines which are not parallel and which do not meet are known as *skew* lines. In a plane two distinct lines are either parallel or intersecting, but in three dimensions there are three possibilities: the lines may be parallel, or intersecting, or skew. The next example illustrates a method of finding whether two lines meet, and if they do meet, the co-ordinates of the intersection point. A very similar method can be used if the lines are specified by their vector equations instead of their cartesian equations.

EXAMPLE 3.9

The lines l_1 and l_2 are represented by the equations

$$l_1: \frac{x-1}{1} = \frac{y+6}{2} = \frac{z+1}{3} \qquad l_2: \frac{x-9}{2} = \frac{y-7}{3} = \frac{z-2}{-1}.$$

Find whether the lines meet, and, if so, the co-ordinates of their common point.

SOLUTION

If there is a point (X, Y, Z) common to both lines then

$$\frac{X-1}{1} = \frac{Y+6}{2} = \frac{Z+1}{3} = \lambda, \text{ say, and } \frac{X-9}{2} = \frac{Y-7}{3} = \frac{Z-2}{-1} = \mu, \text{ say.}$$

Writing X, Y and Z in terms of the parameters λ and μ, gives

$$X = \lambda + 1 = 2\mu + 9 \qquad \text{①}$$

$$Y = 2\lambda - 6 = 3\mu + 7 \qquad \text{②}$$

$$Z = 3\lambda - 1 = -\mu + 2 \qquad \text{③}$$

Now solve any two of the three equations above simultaneously.

In this example we use ① and ②:

$$\left. \begin{aligned} \lambda - 2\mu &= 8 \\ 2\lambda - 3\mu &= 13 \end{aligned} \right\} \Leftrightarrow \left\{ \begin{aligned} 2\lambda - 4\mu &= 16 \\ 2\lambda - 3\mu &= 13 \end{aligned} \right\} \Leftrightarrow \mu = -3, \lambda = 2.$$

If these solutions satisfy the previously unused equation (equation ③ here) then the lines do meet, and our value of λ (or value of μ) substituted into equations ①, ② and ③ gives us the co-ordinates (X, Y, Z) of the common point.

If our values of λ and μ do not fit the third (previously unused) equation then the lines do not meet.

As $\lambda = 2 \Rightarrow Z = 3\lambda - 1 = 5$ and $\mu = -3 \Rightarrow Z = -\mu + 2 = 5$, the values $\lambda = 2$ and $\mu = -3$ satisfy equation ③, as well as equations ① and ②, proving that the lines meet.

Using $\lambda = 2$ or $\mu = -3$ in equations ①, ② and ③ gives $X = 3$, $Y = -2$, $Z = 5$. The lines meet at the point $(3, -2, 5)$.

The cartesian equations of line l_2 in the last example were

$$\frac{x-9}{2} = \frac{y-7}{3} = \frac{z-2}{-1}.$$

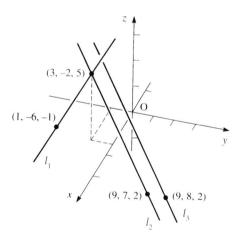

Figure 3.12

If you replace $y - 7$ by $y - 8$ in the equations, you translate line l_2 one unit parallel to the y axis, forming line l_3 (figure 3.12). You would not expect lines l_1 and l_3 to intersect.

EXAMPLE 3.10

Prove that the lines l_1 and l_3 do not meet, where

$$l_1: \frac{x-1}{1} = \frac{y+6}{2} = \frac{z+1}{3} \qquad l_3: \frac{x-9}{2} = \frac{y-8}{3} = \frac{z-2}{-1}.$$

SOLUTION

If there is a point (X, Y, Z) common to both lines then

$$\frac{X-1}{1} = \frac{Y+6}{2} = \frac{Z+1}{3} = \lambda, \text{ say, and } \frac{X-9}{2} = \frac{Y-8}{3} = \frac{Z-2}{-1} = \mu, \text{ say.}$$

Writing X, Y and Z in terms of the parameters λ and μ:

$$X = \lambda + 1 = 2\mu + 9 \qquad \qquad ①$$
$$Y = 2\lambda - 6 = 3\mu + 8 \qquad \qquad ②$$
$$Z = 3\lambda - 1 = -\mu + 2 \qquad \qquad ③$$

Solving equations ① and ② simultaneously:

$$\begin{cases} \lambda - 2\mu = 8 \\ 2\lambda - 3\mu = 14 \end{cases} \Leftrightarrow \begin{cases} 2\lambda - 4\mu = 16 \\ 2\lambda - 3\mu = 14 \end{cases} \Leftrightarrow \mu = -2, \lambda = 4.$$

As $\lambda = 4 \Rightarrow Z = 3\lambda - 1 = 11$, but $\mu = -2 \Rightarrow Z = -\mu + 2 = 4$, the values $\lambda = 4$ and $\mu = -2$ do not satisfy equation ③, although they satisfy equations ① and ②, proving that the lines l_1 and l_3 do not meet.

EXERCISE 3C

1 Decide whether the following pairs of lines intersect or not. If they do intersect, find the co-ordinates of the intersection point.

(i) $\dfrac{x-6}{1} = \dfrac{y+4}{-2} = \dfrac{z-2}{5}, \dfrac{x-1}{1} = \dfrac{y-4}{-1} = \dfrac{z+17}{2}$

(ii) $\dfrac{x+1}{2} = \dfrac{y-2}{0} = \dfrac{z-4}{3}, \dfrac{x+4}{5} = \dfrac{y-4}{-2} = \dfrac{z-6}{1}$

(iii) $\dfrac{x}{5} = \dfrac{y+1}{3} = \dfrac{z-4}{-3}, \dfrac{x-2}{4} = \dfrac{y-5}{-3} = \dfrac{z+1}{2}$

(iv) $\mathbf{r} = \begin{pmatrix} 9 \\ 3 \\ -4 \end{pmatrix} + t \begin{pmatrix} 1 \\ 2 \\ -3 \end{pmatrix}, \mathbf{r} = \begin{pmatrix} 1 \\ -4 \\ 5 \end{pmatrix} + t \begin{pmatrix} 1 \\ -1 \\ 2 \end{pmatrix}$

(v) $\mathbf{r} = \begin{pmatrix} 2 \\ 3 \\ 1 \end{pmatrix} + t \begin{pmatrix} 1 \\ 1 \\ -2 \end{pmatrix}, \mathbf{r} = \begin{pmatrix} -1 \\ -3 \\ -1 \end{pmatrix} + t \begin{pmatrix} 1 \\ 3 \\ 2 \end{pmatrix}$

2 To support a tree damaged in a gale a tree surgeon attaches wire guys to four of the branches (see the diagram). He joins $(2, 0, 3)$ to $(-1, 2, 6)$ and $(0, 3, 5)$ to $(-2, -2, 4)$. Do the guys, assumed straight, meet?

3 The line with cartesian equations $\dfrac{x+4}{2} = \dfrac{y-4}{-10} = \dfrac{z+12}{11}$ meets

$\dfrac{x-4}{2} = \dfrac{y+15}{-3} = \dfrac{z+16}{-5}$ at A and meets $\dfrac{x+1}{1} = \dfrac{y+29}{1} = \dfrac{z+3}{8}$ at B.

Find the co-ordinates of A and the length of AB.

4 Show that the three lines $\dfrac{x+7}{4} = \dfrac{y-24}{-7} = \dfrac{z+4}{4}$, $\dfrac{x-3}{2} = \dfrac{y+10}{2} = \dfrac{z-15}{-1}$,

$\dfrac{x+3}{8} = \dfrac{y-6}{-3} = \dfrac{z-6}{2}$ form a triangle, and find the lengths of its sides.

5 The co-ordinates of four points are as follows:

$$A(2, -9, -5), B(5, -4, -4), C(8, 15, 4) \text{ and } D(7, 18, 6).$$

(i) Calculate the vector product $\overrightarrow{AB} \times \overrightarrow{CD}$.

(ii) Show that the lines AB and CD intersect, and find the co-ordinates of the point of intersection.

(iii) Find, in the form $ax + by + cz + d = 0$, the equation of the plane P which contains the points A, B, C and D.

(iv) Find the equation of the plane which contains the line AB and is perpendicular to the plane P.

[MEI]

6 (i) Calculate the vector product $\mathbf{a} \times \mathbf{b}$ when $\mathbf{a} = 6\mathbf{i} - 8\mathbf{j} - 3\mathbf{k}$ and $\mathbf{b} = -6\mathbf{i} + 5\mathbf{j} + 2\mathbf{k}$.

Two straight lines L and M are given by the equations

$$L: \quad \dfrac{x-1}{6} = \dfrac{y+2}{-8} = \dfrac{z-5}{-3}$$

$$M: \quad \dfrac{x-7}{-6} = \dfrac{y-2}{5} = \dfrac{z-h}{2}$$

where (x, y, z) are cartesian co-ordinates and h is a constant.
The lines L and M intersect.

(ii) Find the value of h and the co-ordinates of the point of intersection of L and M.

(iii) Find, in the form $ax + by + cz + d = 0$, the equation of the plane P containing the lines L and M.
(You may find your answer to part (i) helpful.)

(iv) Explain why the line with equation $\dfrac{x-12}{6} = \dfrac{y+4}{-8} = \dfrac{z-9}{-3}$ is parallel

to the plane P, and calculate the shortest distance between this line and the plane.

[MEI]

7 Lines l_1 and l_2 are skew, and X is a point on neither l_1 nor l_2. By considering the plane containing both l_1 and X, or otherwise, prove that if there is a line through X intersecting both l_1 and l_2, then it is unique.

8 (i) Show that the lines $l_1: \dfrac{x+1}{3} = \dfrac{y+4}{-4} = \dfrac{z-5}{7}$ and $l_2: \dfrac{x-12}{0} = \dfrac{y}{2} = \dfrac{z-2}{-3}$ are skew.

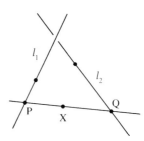

(ii) The points P and Q are on lines l_1 and l_2 respectively. Write down the co-ordinates of P and Q in terms of parameters p and q respectively.

(iii) The line PQ passes through the point $X(8, 6, -8)$. Use the fact that $\overrightarrow{XP} = \lambda\overrightarrow{XQ}$ to find the equation of PQ (in any form).

(iv) Find the co-ordinates of P and Q.

9 (i) A cube has side a. Show that the vertices are $\frac{1}{2}a\sqrt{3}$ from the centre of the cube.

(ii) Points A and B have co-ordinates $(3, 3, 3)$ and $(5, -1, -1)$ respectively. Show that $OA = OB = \frac{1}{2}\sqrt{3}AB$.

(iii) A and B are adjacent vertices of a cube which has its centre at the origin. Find the co-ordinates of the other vertices.

10 (i) Show that the lines $l_1: \dfrac{x-11}{2} = \dfrac{y+9}{1} = \dfrac{z-25}{2}$ and $l_2: \dfrac{x-4}{2} = \dfrac{y-15}{-6} = \dfrac{z-5}{-5}$ are skew.

(ii) The points P and Q are on lines l_1 and l_2 respectively, such that PQ is perpendicular to both l_1 and l_2. Find a vector parallel to PQ and a vector perpendicular to both PQ and l_2.

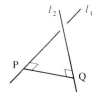

(iii) Find the equation of the plane π that contains both PQ and l_2.

(iv) Find where l_1 meets π.

(v) Find the cartesian equations of PQ.

(vi) Find the co-ordinates of Q and the shortest distance between lines l_1 and l_2.

11 In a chemical plant a straight pipe connects $A(-2, 32, -3)$ and $B(23, 57, -23)$ and a second straight pipe connects $C(25, 3, 14)$ and $D(49, 30, -1)$, where axes are scaled in metres. Use the methods described in Question 10 to find the length of the shortest straight pipe that would connect AB to CD, and the co-ordinates of the necessary junction points.

1 The vector product of **a** and **b** is $\mathbf{a} \times \mathbf{b} = |\mathbf{a}||\mathbf{b}|\sin\theta\hat{\mathbf{n}}$, where θ is the angle between **a** and **b**, and $\hat{\mathbf{n}}$ is a unit vector which is perpendicular to both **a** and **b**, and such that **a**, **b**, $\hat{\mathbf{n}}$ is a right-handed set.

2 $\mathbf{a} \times \mathbf{b} = \begin{pmatrix} a_1 \\ a_2 \\ a_3 \end{pmatrix} \times \begin{pmatrix} b_1 \\ b_2 \\ b_3 \end{pmatrix} = \begin{pmatrix} a_2 b_3 - a_3 b_2 \\ a_3 b_1 - a_1 b_3 \\ a_1 b_2 - a_2 b_1 \end{pmatrix}.$

3 The vector product is anti-commutative:

$$\mathbf{a} \times \mathbf{b} = -\mathbf{b} \times \mathbf{a}$$

and distributive over vector addition:

$$\mathbf{a} \times (\mathbf{b} + \mathbf{c}) = \mathbf{a} \times \mathbf{b} + \mathbf{a} \times \mathbf{c}.$$

4 To find the equations of l, the line of intersection of the planes

$$a_1 x + a_2 y + a_3 z = a_4 \quad \text{and} \quad b_1 x + b_2 y + b_3 z = b_4$$

- find a point P on l by choosing a value for one of x, y, or z, substituting this into both equations, and then solving simultaneously to find the other two variables;
- *either* find a second point Q on l, as above and use $\overrightarrow{PQ}$ as **d**, the direction vector of l

    or use $\mathbf{a} \times \mathbf{b}$ as **d**, the direction vector of l, where

$$\mathbf{a} = \begin{pmatrix} a_1 \\ a_2 \\ a_3 \end{pmatrix} \quad \text{and} \quad \mathbf{b} = \begin{pmatrix} b_1 \\ b_2 \\ b_3 \end{pmatrix}$$

    are the normals to the two planes;
- then write down the vector equation or the cartesian equations of l.

5 The angle between two planes is the same as the angle between their normals.

6 To find the intersection point of the lines

$$\frac{x - x_1}{d_1} = \frac{y - y_1}{e_1} = \frac{z - z_1}{f_1} \quad \text{and} \quad \frac{x - x_2}{d_2} = \frac{y - y_2}{e_2} = \frac{z - z_2}{f_2}$$

- express the co-ordinates of points on the lines in terms of parameters λ and μ:

$$\begin{aligned} x &= d_1 \lambda + x_1 &= d_2 \mu + x_2 \\ y &= e_1 \lambda + y_1 &= e_2 \mu + y_2 \\ z &= f_1 \lambda + z_1 &= f_2 \mu + z_2 \end{aligned}$$

- solve two of the equations simultaneously for λ and μ, and check whether the solution satisfies the third equation;
- if the values found for λ and μ satisfy all three equations the corresponding values of x, y, z are the co-ordinates of the point where the lines intersect;
- if the values found for λ and μ do not satisfy the third equation the lines do not intersect.

Induction and series

The distance does not matter; it is only the first step that is difficult.

Marquise du Deffand (1763)

Induction in mathematics

1 Work out the first four terms of this pattern:

$$1^2 =$$

$$1^2 - 2^2 + 3^2 =$$

$$1^2 - 2^2 + 3^2 - 4^2 + 5^2 =$$

... ...

Look carefully at your answers (in particular their factors), and *predict* the next two terms. Then check your predictions.

2 Work out the value of

$$1 + {}^nC_2 + {}^nC_4$$

for $n = 1, 2, 3, 4$. Look carefully at your answers, and *predict* the values for $n = 5, 6$. Then check your predictions.

(Reminder: ${}^nC_r = \dfrac{n!}{r!(n-r)!}$ for $n \geq r$, and ${}^nC_r = 0$ for $n < r$.)

It is not possible to prove something until you know what you want to prove: the systematic organisation comes *after* the result is known. Mathematical discovery does not usually come by logical deduction; new truths are more often found by experiment with particular examples, by analogy, by intuition, or just 'out of the blue' (though inspiration is unlikely to come without a good deal of hard work to prepare the ground).

The two activities you have just done illustrate one common way of making progress in mathematics. The examination of a number of particular cases suggests a pattern, which can usually be put into algebra to form a *conjecture* (i.e. a guess) about a more general result. This investigative process is called *induction*.

The conjecture can then be tested in further particular cases. If you find a *counter-example* (a case where the conjecture is not true) then the conjecture is definitely disproved. For example, if in the last activity you made the obvious prediction $1 + {}^nC_2 + {}^nC_4 = 2^{n-1}$ you will have found that $n = 6$ gives a counter-example, so the conjecture is wrong.

If, on the other hand, the further particular cases agree with the conjecture you may well feel that you are on the right lines, but you can never be certain that further trial might not reveal a counter-example: the conjecture has been confirmed, but not proved.

To illustrate how we can get beyond this stage, we look more closely at the first activity above. This involves the alternating sum of an odd number of squares.

If there are $(2n - 1)$ squares this sum is

$$1^2 - 2^2 + 3^2 - 4^2 + 5^2 - ... - (2n - 2)^2 + (2n - 1)^2$$

This activity has shown that the conjecture

$$1^2 - 2^2 + 3^2 - 4^2 + 5^2 - ... - (2n - 2)^2 + (2n - 1)^2 = n(2n - 1) \qquad \text{(C)}$$

is true for $n = 1, 2, ..., 6$. We call this conjecture (C), and we want to prove that it is true for *all* positive integers n. It is not easy to see how to do this by deduction from known results, so we use a different approach.

If (C) is true for a particular integer, $n = k$ say, then

$$1^2 - 2^2 + 3^2 - 4^2 + 5^2 - ... - (2k - 2)^2 + (2k - 1)^2 = k(2k - 1).$$

Subtracting the next square and adding the one after that gives

$$1^2 - 2^2 + 3^2 - 4^2 + 5^2 - ... - (2k - 2)^2 + (2k - 1)^2 - (2k)^2 + (2k + 1)^2$$
$$= k(2k - 1) - (2k)^2 + (2k + 1)^2.$$

If (C) is also true for the next integer, $n = k + 1$, then this right-hand side should equal the right-hand side of (C) with $k + 1$ substituted for n, i.e.

$$(k + 1)(2(k + 1) - 1) = (k + 1)(2k + 1).$$

The next task is to show that this is correct:

$$k(2k - 1) - (2k)^2 + (2k + 1)^2 = 2k^2 - k - 4k^2 + 4k^2 + 4k + 1$$
$$= 2k^2 + 3k + 1$$
$$= (k + 1)(2k + 1)$$

as we wanted.

Since (C) is true when $n = 6$ it follows (taking $k = 6$) that (C) is true when $n = 7$; hence (taking $k = 7$) (C) is true when $n = 8$, and so on. By stepping on like this we can reach any positive integer n however great, so we have proved that (C) is true for *every* positive integer.

This form of proof can be compared with the process of climbing a ladder: if we can **1** reach the bottom rung and **2** get from one rung to the next, then we can climb as far as we like up the ladder (figure 4.1).

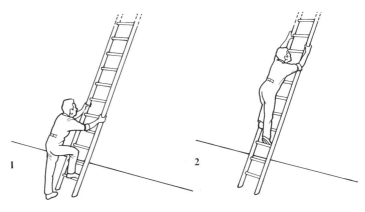

Figure 4.1

The corresponding stages in the proof are

1 showing that (C) is true for $n = 1$ (though in fact you checked it up to $n = 6$);

2 showing that if (C) is true for any particular value of n, $n = k$ say, then it is true for the next value, $n = k + 1$.

This method of proof is called *proof by mathematical induction* (or just *proof by induction*). The word induction is used here because this is a powerful way to prove many of the conjectures which can be found by the sort of inductive investigation which started this section. Here is a more formal statement of the method, plus some more examples.

Proof by mathematical induction

The method of proof by induction can be summarised as follows.

A conjecture (C) involving the positive integer n is true for all n provided that

1 (C) is true when $n = 1$;

2 if (C) is true when $n = k$, then (C) is true when $n = k + 1$.

Both these statements must be proved. Since 1 is usually a simple verification, whereas 2 can be quite complicated, there is a danger that you will concentrate on 2 and forget about 1 – but it is no use being able to climb the ladder if you cannot reach the bottom rung!

ACTIVITY

1 Let (C) be the conjecture

$$2 + 4 + 6 + \dots + 2n = (n + \tfrac{1}{2})^2$$

Prove that if (C) is true when $n = k$ then (C) is true when $n = k + 1$.
Explain why (C) is not true for any positive integer n.

2 Find a conjecture for which statement 1 is true, but 2 is not.

EXAMPLE 4.1

Prove that for all positive integers n

$$1^2 + 2^2 + 3^2 + \ldots + n^2 = \tfrac{1}{6}n(n+1)(2n+1) \quad\text{(C)}$$

SOLUTION

1 The statement (C) is true when $n = 1$, since $1^2 = \tfrac{1}{6} \times 1 \times 2 \times 3$.

2 If (C) is true when $n = k$, that is if

Target: $\tfrac{1}{6}(k+1)(k+2)(2k+3)$

$$1^2 + 2^2 + 3^2 + \ldots + k^2 = \tfrac{1}{6}k(k+1)(2k+1)$$

then $1^2 + 2^2 + 3^2 + \ldots + k^2 + (k+1)^2 = \tfrac{1}{6}k(k+1)(2k+1) + (k+1)^2$

$$= (k+1)\left[\tfrac{1}{6}k(2k+1) + k + 1\right]$$

$$= \tfrac{1}{6}(k+1)\left[k(2k+1) + 6k + 6\right]$$

$$= \tfrac{1}{6}(k+1)(2k^2 + 7k + 6)$$

$$= \tfrac{1}{6}(k+1)(k+2)(2k+3)$$

so that (C) is true when $n = k+1$.

From **1** and **2** by induction (C) is true for all $n \geqslant 1$.

Note

In the rather complicated manipulation in part **2** of this proof we have to reach the right-hand side of (C) with n replaced by $k+1$. It is worth making a note of this target before starting the heavy algebra, to guide the working: for example, in this case, the target shows that it is a good idea to keep $\tfrac{1}{6}(k+1)$ as a factor and then sort out the rest of the expression.

EXAMPLE 4.2

Prove that $y = x^n \Rightarrow \dfrac{\mathrm{d}y}{\mathrm{d}x} = nx^{n-1}$ for all integers $n \geqslant 1$. (C)

SOLUTION

1 (C) is true when $n = 1$ since $y = x \Rightarrow \dfrac{\mathrm{d}y}{\mathrm{d}x} = 1 = 1x^0$.

2 By writing x^{k+1} as $x \times x^k$ and using the method of differentiating a product we have

$$y = x^{k+1} \Rightarrow \dfrac{\mathrm{d}y}{\mathrm{d}x} = x \times \dfrac{\mathrm{d}}{\mathrm{d}x}(x^k) + 1 \times x^k$$

So if (C) is true when $n = k$ then

$$y = x^{k+1} \Rightarrow \dfrac{\mathrm{d}y}{\mathrm{d}x} = x \times kx^{k-1} + 1 \times x^k$$

Target: $(k+1)x^k$

$$= kx^k + x^k$$

$$= (k+1)x^k$$

and therefore (C) is true when $n = k+1$.

From **1** and **2** by induction (C) is true for all $n \geqslant 1$.

EXAMPLE 4.3 Given that z^* is the conjugate of the complex number z, prove that

$$(z^n)^* = (z^*)^n \text{ for all positive integers } n. \tag{C}$$

SOLUTION

1 (C) is true when $n = 1$ since $(z^1)^* = (z^*)^1 = z^*$.

2 From the general property $(z_1 z_2)^* = z_1^* z_2^*$ (see page 26) it follows that $(z^{k+1})^* = (z^k z)^* = (z^k)^* z^*$.

If (C) is true when $n = k$ then $(z^k)^* = (z^*)^k$

and so $(z^{k+1})^* = (z^k)^* z^*$
$$= (z^*)^k z^*$$
$$= (z^*)^{k+1}$$

and therefore (C) is true when $n = k + 1$.

From **1** and **2** by induction (C) is true for all $n \geqslant 1$.

EXERCISE 4A

In Questions 1–8, by considering the first few values of n, suggest a general formula for u_n, and prove your conjecture by mathematical induction.

1 $u_n = 1 + 3 + 5 + \dots + (2n - 1)$.

(This was the first example of proof by induction ever published, by Francesco Maurolycus in 1575.)

2 $u_n = 4 + 7 + 10 + \dots + (3n + 1)$

3 $u_n = \dfrac{1}{1 \times 2} + \dfrac{1}{2 \times 3} + \dfrac{1}{3 \times 4} + \dots + \dfrac{1}{n(n + 1)}$

4 $u_n = \dfrac{1}{3} + \dfrac{1}{15} + \dfrac{1}{35} + \dots + \dfrac{1}{4n^2 - 1}$

5 $u_n = 1 \times 1! + 2 \times 2! + 3 \times 3! + \dots + n \times n!$

6 $u_n = \left(1 - \dfrac{1}{2^2}\right)\left(1 - \dfrac{1}{3^2}\right)\left(1 - \dfrac{1}{4^2}\right) \dots \left(1 - \dfrac{1}{n^2}\right)$

7 $u_{n+1} = \dfrac{u_n}{u_n + 1}, u_1 = 1$

8 $u_{n+1} = 3u_n + 2, u_1 = 2$

9 Prove by induction that $1^3 + 2^3 + 3^3 + \dots + n^3 = \frac{1}{4}n^2(n + 1)^2$.

10 Prove by induction that $1 + x + x^2 + \dots + x^{n-1} = \dfrac{1 - x^n}{1 - x}$ $(x \neq 1)$.

11 Prove that

$$\cos\theta \, \cos2\theta \, \cos4\theta \dots \cos2^n\theta = \dfrac{\sin 2^{n+1}\theta}{2^{n+1}\sin\theta}$$

provided that $\sin\theta \neq 0$.

12 (i) Suppose that $h = a^2 + b^2$ and $k = c^2 + d^2$, where a, b, c, d are integers. Express hk as the sum of two perfect squares.
[**Hint:** Use complex factors and conjugates.]

(ii) Prove by induction that if h can be expressed as the sum of two perfect squares then so can h^n for every positive integer n.

13 Comment on the following 'proof' of the 'theorem':

'In every examination all candidates get the same number of marks'   (T)

Proof by induction on n, the number of candidates.
(i) When $n = 1$ there is only one candidate, so (T) is true.
(ii) Suppose (T) is true when $n = k$. Consider an examination with $k + 1$ candidates A, B, C, D, ... The k candidates B, C, D, ... have the same mark, since (T) is true when $n = k$. Therefore B and C have the same mark. The k candidates A, C, D, ... also have the same mark, so A and C have the same mark. Therefore A, B, C, D, ... all have the same mark, and (T) is true when $n = k + 1$.
From **(i)** and **(ii)** by induction (T) is true for all $n \geqslant 1$.

More proofs by induction

EXAMPLE 4.4

Prove that $u_n = 4^n + 6n - 1$ is divisible by 9 for all $n \geqslant 1$.   (C)

SOLUTION

1 $u_1 = 4 + 6 - 1 = 9$, so (C) is true when $n = 1$.

2 We want to show that u_k is divisible by $9 \Rightarrow u_{k+1}$ is divisible by 9.

Now $u_{k+1} = 4^{k+1} + 6(k + 1) - 1 = 4 \times 4^k + 6k + 5$
$$= 4(4^k + 6k - 1) - 18k + 9$$
$$= 4u_k - 9(2k - 1).$$

Introducing u_k and then compensating

Therefore if u_k is a multiple of 9 then so is u_{k+1}.

From **1** and **2** by induction (C) is true for all $n \geqslant 1$.

Sometimes the method of mathematical induction has to be modified, as illustrated in the next two examples.

EXAMPLE 4.5

The sequence of numbers u_1, u_2, u_3, ... is defined by

$$u_1 = 1, u_2 = 7, u_{n+2} = 7u_{n+1} - 12u_n \quad (n \geqslant 1)$$

Prove that $u_n = 4^n - 3^n$.

SOLUTION

1 Since u_{n+2} depends on the *two* preceding terms of the sequence, we have to show that (C) is true for the first two values of n. When $n = 1$, $4^n - 3^n = 4 - 3 = 1$, and when $n = 2$, $4^n - 3^n = 16 - 9 = 7$, so (C) is true when $n = 1$ and 2.

2 If (C) is true when $n = k$ *and* when $n = k + 1$ then

$$\begin{aligned} u_{k+2} &= 7(4^{k+1} - 3^{k+1}) - 12(4^k - 3^k) \\ &= 7 \times 4^{k+1} - 3 \times 4^{k+1} - 7 \times 3^{k+1} + 4 \times 3^{k+1} \\ &= (7 - 3)4^{k+1} - (7 - 4)3^{k+1} \\ &= 4^{k+2} - 3^{k+2} \end{aligned}$$

so that (C) is true when $n = k + 2$.

Thus if (C) is true for any two consecutive values of n then it is also true for the next value of n. But (C) is true for the consecutive values $n = 1, 2$. Hence by induction (C) is true for all $n \geqslant 1$.

EXAMPLE 4.6

Find the set of positive integers n for which $2^n > n^2$.

SOLUTION

The first few values of n give the following

n	1	2	3	4	5	6
2^n	2	4	8	16	32	64
n^2	1	4	9	16	25	36
$2^n > n^2$?	Yes	No	No	No	Yes	Yes

This suggests that the statement $2^n > n^2$, which we call (C), is true for $n = 1$ and for $n \geqslant 5$.

To prove this, suppose that (C) is true when $n = k$, where $k \geqslant 5$. Then

$$\begin{aligned} 2^k > k^2 \Rightarrow 2^{k+1} &> 2k^2 \quad \text{(multiplying by 2)} \\ &= k^2 + k^2 \\ &\geqslant k^2 + 5k \quad \text{(since } k \geqslant 5) \\ &> k^2 + 2k + 1 \\ &= (k + 1)^2 \end{aligned}$$

Target:
$2^{k+1} > (k + 1)^2$

so that (C) is true when $n = k + 1$. Hence by induction (C) is true for all $n \geqslant 5$ (and also, as the table shows, for $n = 1$).

Note

In Example 4.6 the mathematical induction starts at $n = 5$ instead of the usual $n = 1$. The statement is true when $n = 1$, but the essential step of showing that $2^k > k^2 \Rightarrow 2^{k+1} > (k+1)^2$ does not work until $k \geqslant 3$, and (C) is not true again until $n = 5$.

EXERCISE 4B

1 Examine the divisors of $11^n + 3 \times 4^{n-1}$ for $n = 1, 2, 3, 4$. Form a conjecture based on this evidence, and prove it by induction.

2 Prove that $11^{n+2} + 12^{2n+1}$ is divisible by 133 for $n \geqslant 0$.

3 Prove, using the method of mathematical induction, that $2^{4n+1} + 3$ is a multiple of 5 for any positive integer n.

[MEI, part]

4 Given that $u_{n+1} = 4u_n - 6$, find, with proof, an expression for u_n
   (i) when $u_1 = 2$;
   (ii) when $u_1 = 3$.

5 A sequence of integers $u_1, u_2, u_3, \ldots$ is defined by

$$u_1 = 5 \text{ and } u_{n+1} = 3u_n - 2^n \text{ for } n \geqslant 1.$$

   (i) Use this definition to find u_2 and u_3.
   (ii) Prove by induction that $u_n = 2^n + 3^n$ for all positive integers n.

[MEI, part]

6 A sequence of complex numbers $z_1, z_2, z_3, \ldots$ is defined by $z_1 = 1 - 2j$ and

$$z_{n+1} = \frac{z_n^2 + 2z_n + 5n^2}{2n} \text{ for } n \geqslant 1.$$

   (i) Show that $z_2 = 2z_1$.
   (ii) Prove by induction that $z_n = n - 2nj$.

[MEI, part]

7 Given that $u_{n+2} = 10u_{n+1} - 25u_n$ with $u_1 = 0$ and $u_2 = 1$, prove that $u_n = (n-1)5^{n-2}$.

8 Given that $u_{n+2} = 6u_{n+1} - 4u_n$ with $u_1 = 6$ and $u_2 = 28$, prove that $u_n = (3 + \sqrt{5})^n + (3 - \sqrt{5})^n$.

Deduce that, for $n > 1$, the integer nearest to $(3 + \sqrt{5})^n$ is divisible by 2^n.

9 Find the smallest integer N for which $3^n < n!$. Prove that $3^n < n!$ for all $n \geqslant N$.

10 Find, with proof, the set of positive integers n for which $2^n > n^3$.

11 The arithmetic (A) and geometric (G) means of a set of n positive real numbers $x_1, x_2, ..., x_n$ are

$$A = \frac{x_1 + x_2 + ... + x_n}{n} \quad \text{and} \quad G = \sqrt[n]{x_1 x_2 ... x_n}\,.$$

Let (C) be the statement that $A \geqslant G$. This is a famous inequality which has many different proofs. The method outlined here shows an interesting variant of standard induction:

(C) is proved first for $n = 2^m$, and then the gaps between the powers of 2 are filled by stepping backwards.

(i) By considering $\left(\sqrt{x_1} - \sqrt{x_2}\right)^2$, prove that (C) is true when $n = 2$.

(ii) By letting $y_r = \dfrac{x_{2r-1} + x_{2r}}{2}$ and considering the arithmetic mean of the y_r, prove that if (C) is true when $n = k$ when (C) is true when $n = 2k$. Deduce that (C) is true when $n = 2^m$.

(iii) By considering the k numbers $x_1, x_2, ..., x_{k-1}, \dfrac{x_1 + x_2 + ... + x_{k-1}}{k-1}$, prove that if (C) is true when $n = k$ then (C) is true when $n = k - 1$.

(iv) Deduce that (C) is true for all integers $n \geqslant 2$. Under what conditions is there equality in (C)?

Summation of finite series

The sum S_n of a finite series is found by adding together the first n terms of a finite sequence. If the rth term of the sequence is u_r then

$$S_n = u_1 + u_2 + ... + u_n = \sum_{r=1}^{n} u_r$$

In earlier components you have already met these important examples:

Arithmetic series: $\quad u_r = a + (r-1)d \qquad S_n = \frac{1}{2}n\,[2a + (n-1)d]$

Geometric series: $\quad u_r = ax^{r-1} \qquad\qquad S_n = \dfrac{a(1 - x^n)}{1 - x}$

Binomial series: $\quad u_r = {}^nC_r x^r \qquad\qquad S_n = (1 + x)^n - 1$

Note that the binomial expansion of $(1 + x)^n$ has $n + 1$ terms, starting with $u_0 = 1$; this has to be subtracted to give S_n.

As you have seen in the previous section, if you can guess what the sum of a series is you can often prove it by mathematical induction. Here are some other ways of dealing with finite sums. Some of these results will be familiar to you; the important thing is to concentrate on the methods of obtaining them.

EXAMPLE 4.7

Find $\displaystyle\sum_{r=1}^{n} r.$

SOLUTION

The series is just the sum of the first n positive integers, which can be found easily as the sum of an arithmetic series. But as an alternative you can use the ancient Greek idea of triangle numbers. The nth triangle number, T_n, is the number of dots in a triangular array having n rows, with 1 dot on the top row, 2 dots on the second row, 3 dots on the third row, and so on (see figure 4.2).

So the sum you want is simply T_n. But the triangle for T_n can be put next to a congruent inverted triangle to form a rectangle with n rows and $(n + 1)$ columns as shown in figure 4.3 for the case $n = 5$.

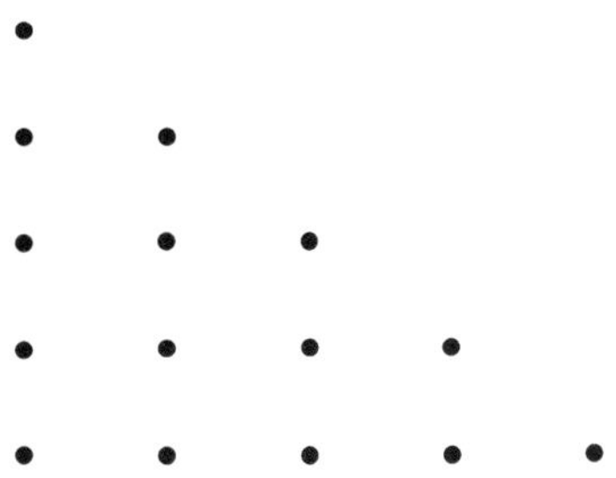

Figure 4.2 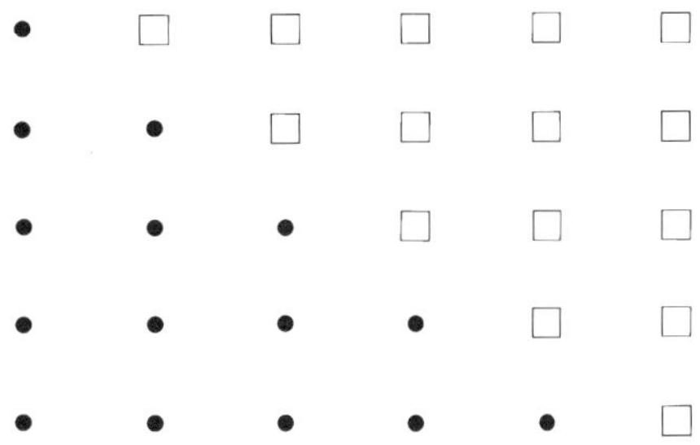   **Figure 4.3**

The number of dots in this rectangle is $n(n + 1)$, so that $\displaystyle T_n = \sum_{r=1}^{n} r = \tfrac{1}{2}n(n + 1).$

EXAMPLE 4.8

Find $\displaystyle\sum_{r=1}^{n} r^2 .$

SOLUTION

The formula has already been proved by induction in Example 4.1. Here we use a more direct method which does not depend upon knowing the answer. The starting point for this proof is not obvious, but your ability to spot such devices should grow with practice.

You start with the difference between two binomial expansions in which the odd powers cancel:

$$(2r + 1)^3 - (2r - 1)^3 \equiv 8r^3 + 12r^2 + 6r + 1 - (8r^3 - 12r^2 + 6r - 1) \equiv 24r^2 + 2.$$

Swapping the right- and left-hand sides and substituting $r = 1, 2, 3, ..., n$ successively gives

$$24 \times 1^2 + 2 = 3^3 - 1^3$$
$$24 \times 2^2 + 2 = 5^3 - 3^3$$
$$24 \times 3^2 + 2 = 7^3 - 5^3$$

... ...

$$24 \times n^2 + 2 = (2n + 1)^3 - (2n - 1)^3$$

When these n equations are added together all except two of the cubes on the right-hand side cancel, giving

$$24 \sum_{r=1}^{n} r^2 + 2n = (2n + 1)^3 - 1^3$$

$$\Rightarrow \quad 24 \sum_{r=1}^{n} r^2 = 8n^3 + 12n^2 + 6n + 1 - 1 - 2n$$

$$= 8n^3 + 12n^2 + 4n$$

$$= 4n(2n^2 + 3n + 1)$$

$$= 4n(n + 1)(2n + 1)$$

$$\Rightarrow \quad \sum_{r=1}^{n} r^2 = \tfrac{1}{6}n(n + 1)(2n + 1).$$

Example 4.8 illustrates a useful method for summing series, called the *method of differences*. The idea is to express each term u_r of the sum as the difference of consecutive terms of another sequence, i e. to find v_r such that

$$u_r = v_{r-1} - v_r \quad \text{for} \quad r = 1, 2, 3, \dots, n.$$

Then $\displaystyle\sum_{r=1}^{n} u_r = (v_0 - v_1) + (v_1 - v_2) + (v_2 - v_3) + \dots + (v_{n-1} - v_n).$

On the right-hand side all but two of the v_r cancel, leaving only $v_0 - v_n$.

Therefore $\displaystyle\sum_{r=1}^{n} u_r = v_0 - v_n.$

The cancelling of nearly all the v_r is similar to the way in which the interior sections of a collapsible telescope disappear when it is compressed, so this can be described as a *telescoping sum*.

ACTIVITY

1   Prove formally by induction that if $u_r = v_{r-1} - v_r$ for $r = 1, 2, 3, \dots, n$ then

$$\sum_{r=1}^{n} u_r = v_0 - v_n.$$

2   What v_r was used in the solution of Example 4.8?

3   By taking $v_r = r(r + 1)(r + 2)$ and using the method of differences, find $\displaystyle\sum_{r=1}^{n} r(r + 1).$

EXAMPLE 4.9

Find $\displaystyle\sum_{r=1}^{n} \frac{1}{r(r+1)}$.

SOLUTION

By partial fractions $\dfrac{1}{r(r+1)} = \dfrac{1}{r} - \dfrac{1}{r+1}$

so $\displaystyle\sum_{r=1}^{n} \frac{1}{r(r+1)} = \left(1 - \frac{1}{2}\right) + \left(\frac{1}{2} - \frac{1}{3}\right) + \left(\frac{1}{3} - \frac{1}{4}\right) + \dots + \left(\frac{1}{n} - \frac{1}{n+1}\right)$

$$= 1 - \frac{1}{n+1} = \frac{n}{n+1}.$$

Example 4.9 uses the method of differences with $v_r = \dfrac{1}{r+1}$. The next example uses a rather more complicated telescoping sum.

EXAMPLE 4.10

Find $\displaystyle\sum_{r=1}^{n} \frac{r+4}{r(r+1)(r+2)}$.

SOLUTION

By partial fractions $\dfrac{r+4}{r(r+1)(r+2)} = \dfrac{2}{r} - \dfrac{3}{r+1} + \dfrac{1}{r+2}$, so

$$\sum_{r=1}^{n} \frac{r+4}{r(r+1)(r+2)} = 2 - \frac{3}{2} + \frac{1}{3}$$

$$+ \frac{2}{2} - \frac{3}{3} + \frac{1}{4}$$

$$+ \frac{2}{3} - \frac{3}{4} + \frac{1}{5}$$

$$+ \dots \dots$$

$$+ \frac{2}{n-2} - \frac{3}{n-1} + \frac{1}{n}$$

$$+ \frac{2}{n-1} - \frac{3}{n} + \frac{1}{n+1}$$

$$+ \frac{2}{n} - \frac{3}{n+1} + \frac{1}{n+2}$$

Everything in here cancels

Most of the terms cancel, leaving

$$\sum_{r=1}^{n} \frac{r+4}{r(r+1)(r+2)} = 2 - \frac{3}{2} + \frac{2}{2} + \frac{1}{n+1} - \frac{3}{n+1} + \frac{1}{n+2}$$

$$= \frac{3}{2} - \frac{2}{n+1} + \frac{1}{n+2}$$

$$= \frac{n(3n+7)}{2(n+1)(n+2)}.$$

Note

The terms which do not cancel form a symmetrical pattern, three at the start and three at the end.

In Question 9 of Exercise 4A you proved that $\sum_{r=1}^{n} r^3 = \frac{1}{4}n^2(n+1)^2$, and Example 4.7 shows that $\sum_{r=1}^{n} r = \frac{1}{2}n(n+1)$. It follows that

$$\sum_{r=1}^{n} r^3 = \left(\sum_{r=1}^{n} r \right)^2.$$

This is really just a curiosity, though it does make it easy to remember the formula for the sum of cubes. The following geometrical proof of the same result may appeal to you.

Since $r^3 = r \times r^2$, we represent the cube r^3 not as a volume but as the area of r squares of side r, so that the sum of cubes is the total area of

    1 square of side 1 + 2 squares of side 2 + 3 squares of side 3 + ...
    + n squares of side n.

These can be arranged as shown (for $n = 5$, but the pattern continues) in figure 4.4.

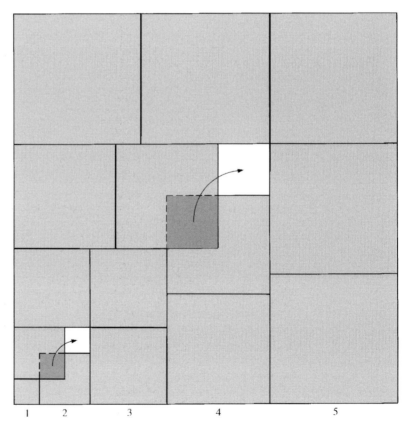

Figure 4.4

The even-sided squares overlap, but there is a gap (unshaded) of exactly the same size as the overlap, so the overlapping regions can be moved to fill the gaps. Therefore the squares exactly fill a large square, whose side is $(1 + 2 + 3 + ... + n)$, which is what we set out to prove.

The three important results

$$\sum_{r=1}^{n} r = \tfrac{1}{2}n(n + 1) \qquad \sum_{r=1}^{n} r^2 = \tfrac{1}{6}n(n + 1)(2n + 1) \qquad \sum_{r=1}^{n} r^3 = \tfrac{1}{4}n^2(n + 1)^2$$

can be used to sum further series, as in the following examples.

EXAMPLE 4.11 Find $\displaystyle\sum_{r=1}^{n} r(r + 2)$.

SOLUTION

$$\sum_{r=1}^{n} r(r + 2) = \sum_{r=1}^{n} (r^2 + 2r) = \sum_{r=1}^{n} r^2 + 2 \sum_{r=1}^{n} r$$

$$= \tfrac{1}{6}n(n + 1)(2n + 1) + 2 \times \tfrac{1}{2}n(n + 1)$$

$$= \tfrac{1}{6}n(n + 1)(2n + 1 + 6)$$

$$= \tfrac{1}{6}n(n + 1)(2n + 7)$$

EXAMPLE 4.12 Find the sum of the first n odd cubes.

SOLUTION

The rth odd number is $(2r - 1)$, so what we want is $\displaystyle\sum_{r=1}^{n} (2r - 1)^3$.

Since $(2r - 1)^3 = 8r^3 - 12r^2 + 6r - 1$, the required sum equals

$$8\sum_{r=1}^{n} r^3 - 12\sum_{r=1}^{n} r^2 + 6\sum_{r=1}^{n} r - n$$

and you can substitute the known formula for each of the three sums involved and simplify. This is straightforward, though the algebra is rather tedious.

A simpler alternative is to notice that the sum of the first n odd cubes equals the sum of the first $2n$ cubes minus the sum of the first n even cubes.

The sum of the first $2n$ cubes is $\tfrac{1}{4}(2n)^2(2n + 1)^2 = n^2(2n + 1)^2$.

The sum of the first n even cubes is

$$2^3 + 4^3 + 6^3 + ... + (2n)^3 = 8(1^3 + 2^3 + 3^3 + ... + n^3)$$
$$= 2n^2(n + 1)^2.$$

Therefore the required sum is

$$n^2(2n + 1)^2 - 2n^2(n + 1)^2 = n^2[(2n + 1)^2 - 2(n + 1)^2]$$
$$= n^2(2n^2 - 1).$$

In Questions 1–4, find $\sum\limits_{r=1}^{n} u_r$, where u_r is the given expression.

1 $2r - 1$

2 $r(3r + 1)$

3 $(r + 1)r^2$

4 $4r^3 - 6r^2 + 4r - 1$

5 Find $1^3 + 2^3 + 4^3 + 5^3 + 7^3 + 8^3 + \ldots + (3n - 2)^3 + (3n - 1)^3$.

6 On a fruit stall a pile of oranges is arranged to form a truncated square pyramid. Each layer is a square, with the lengths of side of successive layers reducing by one orange. The bottom layer measures $2n \times 2n$ oranges, and there are n layers.

Prove that the number of oranges used is $\frac{1}{6}n(2n + 1)(7n + 1)$.

What is the greatest n which uses fewer than 1000 oranges?

7 Cannonballs at a military museum are to be displayed in pyramidal piles. Prove that a triangular pyramid in which each side of the base contains $2n$ cannonballs can be rearranged to give exactly four square pyramids in which each side of the base contains n cannonballs. (In both cases the lengths of side of successive layers reduce by one cannonball.)

8 (i) Prove by induction that $\sum\limits_{r=1}^{n} (5r^4 + r^2) = \frac{1}{2}n^2(n + 1)^2(2n + 1)$.

(ii) Using the result in **(i)**, and the formula for $\sum\limits_{r=1}^{n} r^2$, show that

$$\sum_{r=1}^{n} r^4 = \frac{1}{30}n(n + 1)(2n + 1)(3n^2 + 3n - 1).$$

[MEI, part]

9 (i) Prove, by induction or otherwise, that $\sum\limits_{r=1}^{n} (3r^5 + r^3) = \frac{1}{2}n^3(n + 1)^3$.

(ii) Using the result in **(i)** and the formula for $\sum\limits_{r=1}^{n} r^3$, show that

$$\sum_{r=1}^{n} r^5 = \frac{1}{12}n^2(n + 1)^2(2n^2 + 2n - 1).$$

[MEI]

10 (i) Prove, by induction or otherwise, that $\sum\limits_{r=1}^{n} (r + 1)^2 2^{r-1} = (n^2 + 2)2^n - 2$.

(ii) (a) Express $\dfrac{6}{(r + 1)(r + 3)}$ in partial fractions.

(b) Hence find the sum of n terms of the series $\dfrac{6}{2 \times 4} + \dfrac{6}{3 \times 5} + \dfrac{6}{4 \times 6} + \ldots$

[MEI]

In Questions 11–14, use the method of differences to find $\displaystyle\sum_{r=1}^{n} u_r$ for the given u_r.

11 $\dfrac{1}{r(r+2)}$

12 $\dfrac{r}{(r+2)(r+3)(r+4)}$

13 $\dfrac{1}{r(r+1)(r+2)}$

14 $\dfrac{2r+1}{r^2(r+1)^2}$

15 Use the method of differences with $v_r = -r^2(r+1)^2$ to prove the formula for $\displaystyle\sum_{r=1}^{n} r^3$.

16 (i) Use the method of differences with $v_r = -r(r+1)(r+2)(r+3)$ to find

$$\sum_{r=1}^{n} r(r+1)(r+2).$$

(ii) From the formulae for $\displaystyle\sum_{r=1}^{n} r$, $\displaystyle\sum_{r=1}^{n} r(r+1)$ and $\displaystyle\sum_{r=1}^{n} r(r+1)(r+2)$ make a

conjecture about $\displaystyle\sum_{r=1}^{n} r(r+1)(r+2) \dots (r+k)$ and prove it.

17 Using the idea suggested in the diagram, or otherwise, prove that

$$1 \times n + 2(n-1) + 3(n-2) + \dots + n \times 1 = \tfrac{1}{6}n(n+1)(n+2)$$

18 Use the method of differences to find $\displaystyle\sum_{r=1}^{n} \dfrac{r+2}{2^{r+1}r(r+1)}$.
[**Hint:** Use partial fractions.]

19 Let $T = 1 + 2x + 3x^2 + \dots + nx^{n-1}$ $(x \neq 1)$. Find T
(i) by considering $T - xT$;
(ii) by summing $1 + x + x^2 + \dots + x^n$ and then differentiating.

20 Find the sum to n terms of

$$\frac{1}{x+1} + \frac{2x}{(x+1)(x+2)} + \frac{3x^2}{(x+1)(x+2)(x+3)} + \dots.$$

[**Hint**: $nx^{n-1} = x^{n-1}(x+n) - x^n$]

21 You are given that $y = x^2 e^x$.

(i) Show by induction that, for any positive integer n,

$$\frac{d^n y}{dx^n} = \{n(n-1) + 2nx + x^2\}e^x.$$

(ii) Hence show that, when $x = -2$, $\displaystyle\sum_{n=1}^{N} \frac{d^n y}{dx^n} = \frac{1}{3}N(N-1)(N-5)e^{-2}$.

[MEI]

22 An elegant proof for $\displaystyle\sum_{r=1}^{n} r^2$

(i) Using the array below, or otherwise, prove that

$$r^2 = 1 + 2 + 3 + \dots + (r-1) + r + (r-1) + \dots + 3 + 2 + 1.$$

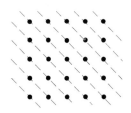

(ii) Show that $\displaystyle\sum_{r=1}^{5} r^2$ is the sum of the numbers in any one of the three arrays below.

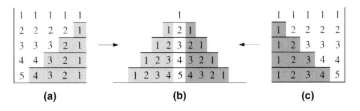

(a)   (b)   (c)

(iii) Now slide **(a)** and **(c)** on top of **(b)** so that they overlap as shown by the shading, and add overlapping numbers. Deduce that

$$3\sum_{r=1}^{5} r^2 = 11 \sum_{r=1}^{5} r.$$

(iv) Generalise this argument to show that

$$3\sum_{r=1}^{n} r^2 = (2n+1)\sum_{r=1}^{n} r$$

and deduce that

$$\sum_{r=1}^{n} r^2 = \frac{1}{6}n(n+1)(2n+1).$$

1 To prove *by induction* that a statement (C) involving an integer n is true for all $n \geqslant n_0$, prove that

   1 (C) is true for $n = n_0$;

   2 if (C) is true for $n = k$ then (C) is true for $n = k + 1$.

   and then bring these parts together to complete the proof.

2 $\displaystyle\sum_{r=1}^{n} r = \tfrac{1}{2}n(n+1)$ $\displaystyle\sum_{r=1}^{n} r^2 = \tfrac{1}{6}n(n+1)(2n+1)$ $\displaystyle\sum_{r=1}^{n} r^3 = \tfrac{1}{4}n^2(n+1)^2$

3 If $u_r = v_{r-1} - v_r$ for $r = 1, 2, ..., n$ then $\displaystyle\sum_{r=1}^{n} u_r = v_0 - v_n$ (a telescoping sum).

   Partial fractions can be useful when finding v_r.

5 Matrices

As for everything else, so for a mathematical theory – beauty can be perceived but not explained.

Arthur Cayley, 1883

Figure 5.1 shows a pack of cards. Initially the cards are piled up neatly forming a cuboid, but two other arrangements are shown.

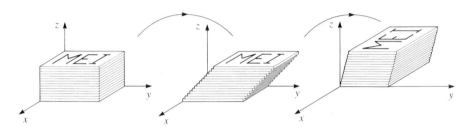

Figure 5.1

 Describe what has happened in words. Can you suggest ways of representing this symbolically?

In this chapter you will learn about matrices, and how they give you the ability to use algebraic techniques in geometrical and other situations. Matrices are often used when creating effects on TV – particularly when the picture is rotated, flipped, enlarged or reduced.

Transformations

In figure 5.2 you will see the effect of various transformations on a standard object. Our standard object includes what is known as the *unit square*, the square with vertices at $(0, 0)$, $(1, 0)$, $(1, 1)$ and $(0, 1)$. In each diagram the point $P'(x', y')$ is the image of $P(x, y)$, and the equations connecting x' and y' with x and y are given. The position and scales of the co-ordinate axes are not changed by the various transformations.

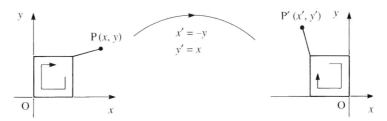

Rotation 90° anticlockwise about O

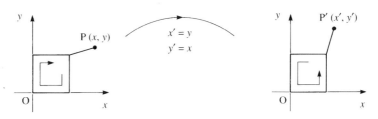

Reflection in the line y = x

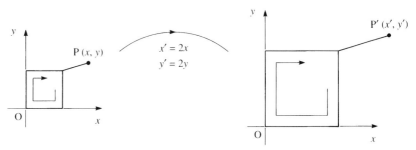

Enlargement, scale factor 2, centre O

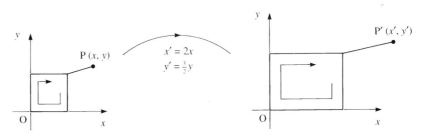

Two-way stretch: ×2 horizontally, ×$\frac{3}{2}$ vertically

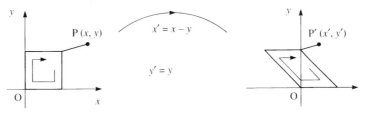

Shear parallel to the x axis

Figure 5.2

Although these transformations cause different changes of shape, size, location, and *sense* (indicated by the arrow inside the unit square reversing from pointing clockwise to pointing anticlockwise) they have similarities. In these examples:

- the image of the unit square is always a parallelogram – rectangles and squares are examples of parallelograms;

- the vertex O of the unit square has not moved.

A further property of these examples is that the co-ordinates of P′ can always be found from the co-ordinates of P using equations of the form

$$\begin{cases} x' = ax + cy \\ y' = bx + dy \end{cases}$$

where a, b, c, d are constants.

You can summarise a pair of equations like these by just noting the array of coefficients: $\begin{pmatrix} a & c \\ b & d \end{pmatrix}$. This array is called the *matrix* of the transformation.

For example, in the two-way stretch, $a = 2$, $b = 0$, $c = 0$, $d = \frac{3}{2}$, and the matrix is $\begin{pmatrix} 2 & 0 \\ 0 & \frac{3}{2} \end{pmatrix}$.

As the shear shown in figure 5.2 is described by the equations $\begin{cases} x' = 1x - 1y \\ y' = 0x + 1y \end{cases}$ its matrix is $\begin{pmatrix} 1 & -1 \\ 0 & 1 \end{pmatrix}$.

ACTIVITY

Write down the matrices which represent

(i)   rotation 90° anticlockwise about O;

(ii) reflection in the line $y = x$;

(iii) enlargement, scale factor 2, centre O.

Example 5.1 shows how you can prove that a transformation may be represented by a matrix in the way just described. It also establishes an important general result about rotations.

EXAMPLE 5.1

Figure 5.3 shows a flag and its image following rotation through angle θ anticlockwise about the origin. The image of the point P(x, y) is P′(x', y'). Find x' and y' in terms of x, y, and θ, and so find the matrix for this rotation.

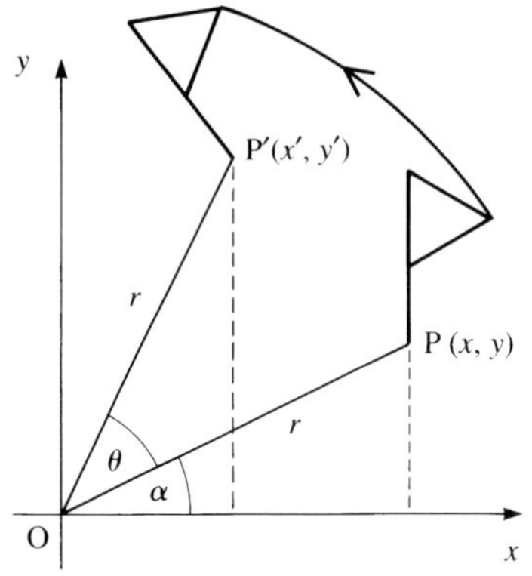

Figure 5.3

SOLUTION

Let OP be of length r.

Rotate OP through angle θ anticlockwise about O. Then

$$x' = r\cos(\alpha + \theta) = r\cos\alpha\cos\theta - r\sin\alpha\sin\theta$$
$$= x\cos\theta - y\sin\theta$$
$$\text{since } x = r\cos\alpha, \ y = r\sin\alpha.$$

Similarly
$$y' = r\sin(\alpha + \theta) = r\sin\alpha\cos\theta + r\cos\alpha\sin\theta$$
$$= x\sin\theta + y\cos\theta.$$

Thus
$$x' = x\cos\theta - y\sin\theta$$
$$y' = x\sin\theta + y\cos\theta$$

and $\begin{pmatrix} \cos\theta & -\sin\theta \\ \sin\theta & \cos\theta \end{pmatrix}$ is the matrix representing a rotation through angle θ anticlockwise about the origin.

Straight lines

Your diagrams have shown the images of straight lines as straight lines. You should assume that any transformation which can be represented by a matrix transforms straight lines into straight lines. (You will prove that this assumption is correct later.) Thus to find the image of the line l through points A and B, find the image A′ of A and the image B′ of B; then the image of l is the line through A′ and B′.

ACTIVITY

A transformation (an example of a *shear*) maps points as follows:

- each point is moved parallel to the x axis;
- each point is moved twice its distance from the x axis;
- points above the x axis are moved to the right;
- points below the x axis are moved to the left.

Figure 5.4 shows a flag, and points P and Q and their images P′ and Q′.

(i) Copy the diagram and draw the image of the flag.

(ii) Show that the image of (x, y) is the point $(x + 2y, y)$ and find the matrix which represents this transformation.

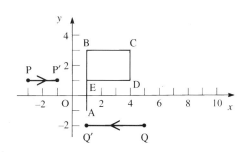

Figure 5.4

The origin does not move

Notice that substituting $x = 0$ and $y = 0$ into $\begin{cases} x' = ax + cy \\ y' = bx + dy \end{cases}$ gives $\begin{cases} x' = 0 \\ y' = 0 \end{cases}$.

This means that whenever you can represent a transformation by a matrix in the way described above, the image of the origin O is O. Thus you can only use this method of representing a transformation if the origin is a point which does not move.

- Rotations can only be represented in this way if the centre of rotation is at O.

- Reflections can only be represented in this way if the mirror line passes through O.

- Enlargements can only be represented in this way if the centre of enlargement is at O.

- Shears can only be represented in this way if each point moves parallel to a line *l* through O, and the distance each point moves is proportional to its distance from *l*.

This may seem to be a considerable restriction – but in practice it is still a very useful procedure!

ACTIVITY

1 Explain why it is not possible to represent translations by matrices in the way described.

2 A shear moves points parallel to the line *l* with equation $y = x$; the distance from a point to its image is proportional to the distance of the point from *l*; the point Q(2, 0) is mapped to Q′(4, 2), as shown in figure 5.5.

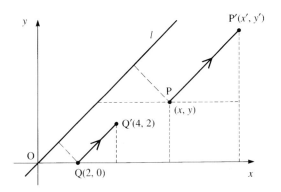

Figure 5.5

The point P has co-ordinates (x, y). By finding the co-ordinates of P′, the image of P, in terms of x and y, show that this shear can be represented by a matrix, and find the matrix.

5

Transformations

The columns of a matrix

Notice the effect of the transformation represented by the matrix $\mathbf{M} = \begin{pmatrix} a & c \\ b & d \end{pmatrix}$ on the points I and J, with position vectors $\begin{pmatrix} 1 \\ 0 \end{pmatrix}$ and $\begin{pmatrix} 0 \\ 1 \end{pmatrix}$:

substituting $x = 1$, $y = 0$ in the defining equations $\begin{cases} x' = ax + cy \\ y' = bx + dy \end{cases}$ you find that I′, the image of I, has position vector $\begin{pmatrix} a \\ b \end{pmatrix}$, which is the first column of matrix $\mathbf{M}$. Similarly J′, the image of J, has position vector $\begin{pmatrix} c \\ d \end{pmatrix}$, the second column of $\mathbf{M}$. This connection between the position vectors of I′ and J′ and the matrix representing a transformation provides you with a quick and usually easy way of finding the matrix. It does not, however, supply any information about whether or not the transformation can be represented by a matrix.

ACTIVITY

Figure 5.6 shows the images of I and J following reflection in the line $y = x\tan\theta$ (i.e. the line through the origin forming an angle θ with the positive x axis). Find the co-ordinates of I′ and J′ and hence show that the matrix which represents this reflection is $\begin{pmatrix} \cos 2\theta & \sin 2\theta \\ \sin 2\theta & -\cos 2\theta \end{pmatrix}$.

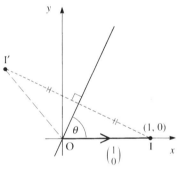

Figure 5.6

EXAMPLE 5.2

A transformation (known as a *projection*) maps each point on to the line *l* in such a way that the line joining a point to its image is perpendicular to *l*. If *l* is the line $y = 2x$ show that the projection can be represented by a matrix, and that the matrix is $\begin{pmatrix} \frac{1}{5} & \frac{2}{5} \\ \frac{2}{5} & \frac{4}{5} \end{pmatrix}$.

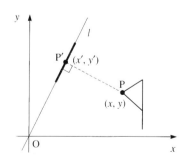

Figure 5.7

83

SOLUTION

$P'(x', y')$ is on $y = 2x$ $\Rightarrow$ $y' = 2x'$.

PP' is perpendicular to $y = 2x$ $\Rightarrow$ gradient of $PP' = -\frac{1}{2}$ so that

$$\frac{y - y'}{x - x'} = -\frac{1}{2} \quad \Rightarrow \quad 2y - 2y' = -x + x'$$

Substituting for y' gives $2y - 4x' = -x + x'$

so that $\qquad\qquad\qquad x' = \frac{1}{5}x + \frac{2}{5}y$

and $\qquad\qquad\qquad\qquad y' = \frac{2}{5}x + \frac{4}{5}y$

showing that the projection can be represented by the matrix $\begin{pmatrix} \frac{1}{5} & \frac{2}{5} \\ \frac{2}{5} & \frac{4}{5} \end{pmatrix}$.

The table opposite illustrates the common transformations of the plane and their matrices.

Transformations in three dimensions

So far your work has been applied to sets of points in a plane (i.e. two dimensions), using the plane as both the domain and co-domain of your transformations. Similar procedures work when you use three-dimensional space as the domain and co-domain.

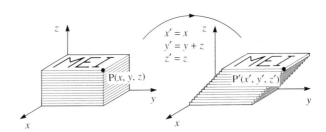

Figure 5.8

The shear illustrated in figure 5.8 is defined by the equations: $\begin{cases} x' = x \\ y' = y + z \\ z' = z \end{cases}$

so you can represent this transformation by the matrix of coefficients $\begin{pmatrix} 1 & 0 & 0 \\ 0 & 1 & 1 \\ 0 & 0 & 1 \end{pmatrix}$.

Transformation		Matrix	Transformation		Matrix
Reflection in x axis		$\begin{pmatrix} 1 & 0 \\ 0 & -1 \end{pmatrix}$	Reflection in y axis		$\begin{pmatrix} -1 & 0 \\ 0 & 1 \end{pmatrix}$
Reflection in $y = -x$		$\begin{pmatrix} 0 & -1 \\ -1 & 0 \end{pmatrix}$	Reflection in $y = x\tan\theta$		$\begin{pmatrix} \cos2\theta & \sin2\theta \\ \sin2\theta & -\cos2\theta \end{pmatrix}$
Rotation 90° anticlockwise about O		$\begin{pmatrix} 0 & -1 \\ 1 & 0 \end{pmatrix}$	Rotation 90° clockwise about O		$\begin{pmatrix} 0 & 1 \\ -1 & 0 \end{pmatrix}$
Half-turn about origin		$\begin{pmatrix} -1 & 0 \\ 0 & -1 \end{pmatrix}$	Rotation θ anticlockwise about origin		$\begin{pmatrix} \cos\theta & -\sin\theta \\ \sin\theta & \cos\theta \end{pmatrix}$
Enlargement $\times k$, centre O		$\begin{pmatrix} k & 0 \\ 0 & k \end{pmatrix}$	Two-way stretch $\times a$ horizontally $\times b$ vertically		$\begin{pmatrix} a & 0 \\ 0 & b \end{pmatrix}$
Shear parallel to x axis, $\times k$		$\begin{pmatrix} 1 & k \\ 0 & 1 \end{pmatrix}$	Shear parallel to y axis, $\times k$		$\begin{pmatrix} 1 & 0 \\ k & 1 \end{pmatrix}$
Projection on to x axis		$\begin{pmatrix} 1 & 0 \\ 0 & 0 \end{pmatrix}$	Projection on to y axis		$\begin{pmatrix} 0 & 0 \\ 0 & 1 \end{pmatrix}$

Reflection in the plane $y = 0$ (figure 5.9) is represented by the matrix $\begin{pmatrix} 1 & 0 & 0 \\ 0 & -1 & 0 \\ 0 & 0 & 1 \end{pmatrix}$.

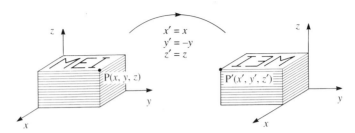

Figure 5.9

It is not necessary for the domain and co-domain of a transformation to be the same. For example, when you draw the plan of a building to a scale of 1 : 100, you start with an object in three-dimensional space and finish with a plane drawing. This might be as illustrated in figure 5.10, in which case the transformation would be represented by the matrix $\begin{pmatrix} \frac{1}{100} & 0 & 0 \\ 0 & \frac{1}{100} & 0 \end{pmatrix}$.

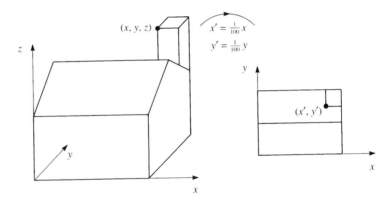

Figure 5.10

A similar transformation is the basis of the geographer's orthographic projection, often used for mapping the polar regions of the world.

Note

The shape of the matrix depends on the dimensions of the domain and co-domain: a matrix with m rows and n columns is used to specify a transformation from n-dimensional space to m-dimensional space, where (for the moment) m and n are restricted to the values 1, 2 and 3.

❓ What is meant by one-dimensional space? Is it part of two-dimensional space? Is two-dimensional space part of three-dimensional space?

1 Draw separate diagrams to show the effect of the following transformations on the object shown below, based on the unit square.

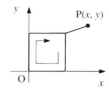

In each case find the co-ordinates of P′, the image of P, in terms of x and y, and hence find the matrix of the transformation.

(i) Enlargement, centre the origin, scale factor 3.

(ii) Reflection in the x axis.

(iii) Reflection in the line $x + y = 0$.

(iv) Rotation 90° clockwise about O.

(v) Enlargement, scale factor $\frac{1}{2}$, centre O.

2 Draw diagrams to show the effect of the transformations represented by the following matrices, and so give full descriptions of the transformations.

(i) $\begin{pmatrix} 1 & 0 \\ 0 & -1 \end{pmatrix}$ **(ii)** $\begin{pmatrix} 0 & 1 \\ 1 & 0 \end{pmatrix}$ **(iii)** $\begin{pmatrix} 2 & 0 \\ 0 & 3 \end{pmatrix}$

(iv) $\begin{pmatrix} 3 & 0 \\ 0 & 3 \end{pmatrix}$ **(v)** $\begin{pmatrix} \frac{1}{\sqrt{2}} & -\frac{1}{\sqrt{2}} \\ \frac{1}{\sqrt{2}} & \frac{1}{\sqrt{2}} \end{pmatrix}$ **(vi)** $\begin{pmatrix} 0.6 & -0.8 \\ 0.8 & 0.6 \end{pmatrix}$

(vii) $\begin{pmatrix} 2 & 0 \\ 0 & \frac{1}{2} \end{pmatrix}$ **(viii)** $\begin{pmatrix} 2 & 1 \\ -1 & 0 \end{pmatrix}$ **(ix)** $\begin{pmatrix} 1 & 0 \\ 0 & 0 \end{pmatrix}$

3 Triangle ABC has its vertices at $(2, 0)$, $(-1, 2)$ and $(1, 4)$. Triangle ABC is mapped to triangle A′B′C′ by the transformation defined by the matrix $\begin{pmatrix} 4 & 3 \\ 5 & 4 \end{pmatrix}$. Find the co-ordinates of A′, B′, and C′ and show that the area of the triangle has not been changed by the transformation.

4 A transformation maps P to P′ as follows:

• each point is mapped on to the line $y = x$;

• the line joining a point to its image is parallel to the y axis.

Find the co-ordinates of the image of the point (x, y) and hence show that this transformation can be represented by means of a matrix. What is that matrix?

5 Plot the points $(1, 0)$, $(1, 2)$, $(2, 2)$, $(2, 1)$, $(1, 1)$ and join them up to form a square flag on a vertical pole. Transform the flag by means of the matrix $\begin{pmatrix} 0 & -1 \\ 1 & 2 \end{pmatrix}$, and show the image on your diagram. Describe the transformation as simply as you can and show that the area of the flag has remained constant.

6 A transformation is represented by the matrix $\begin{pmatrix} 3 & -4 \\ 1 & -1 \end{pmatrix}$.

   (i)   Choosing several points of your own, find the co-ordinates of the image points.

   (ii) Write down the vectors joining each point to its image. What do you notice?

   (iii) Describe this transformation.

7 Find the matrices which represent the following transformations of three-dimensional space:

   (i)   enlargement, centre O, scale factor 3;

   (ii) rotation 180° about the z axis;

   (iii) reflection in the plane $y = z$.

8 Describe the transformations represented by these matrices.

   (i) $\begin{pmatrix} 1 & 0 & 0 \\ 0 & -1 & 0 \\ 0 & 0 & -1 \end{pmatrix}$ (ii) $\begin{pmatrix} 0 & 1 & 0 \\ 1 & 0 & 0 \\ 0 & 0 & 1 \end{pmatrix}$

   (iii) $\begin{pmatrix} 1 & 0 & 3 \\ 0 & 1 & 0 \\ 0 & 0 & 1 \end{pmatrix}$ (iv) $\begin{pmatrix} 0 & 0.01 & 0 \\ 0 & 0 & 0.01 \end{pmatrix}$

Properties of matrices

In the previous section the word ´matrix´ was used for an array of numbers, such as $\begin{pmatrix} 3 & 0 \\ 0 & 1 \end{pmatrix}$, giving information about how to find the position of an image point following a transformation. Although this chapter is mainly concerned with transformation matrices, matrices have many other uses, some of which are explored briefly in Exercise 5B.

Any rectangular array of numbers is known as a matrix. It is usual to represent matrices by capital letters, often in bold print. (In handwriting we often use a capital letter with a line or squiggle under it.)

The order of a matrix

A matrix consists of rows and columns, and the entries in the various cells are known as *elements*. The matrix $\mathbf{M} = \begin{pmatrix} 5 & 1 & 0 \\ 4 & -1 & 3 \end{pmatrix}$ has six elements, arranged in two rows and three columns. We describe $\mathbf{M}$ as a 2×3 matrix, and this is known as the *order* of the matrix. It is important to note that you state the number of rows first, then the number of columns. The column vector $\begin{pmatrix} 1 \\ 0 \end{pmatrix}$ is an example of a 2×1 matrix; the column vector $\begin{pmatrix} 2 \\ -3 \\ 5 \end{pmatrix}$ is a 3×1 matrix. (Column vectors are sometimes called column matrices; they are often represented by lower case bold letters, such as $\mathbf{p}$ or $\mathbf{v}$.)

Matrices such as $\begin{pmatrix} 1 & 3 & -2 \\ -7 & 5 & 4 \\ 9 & 0 & 6 \end{pmatrix}$ and $\begin{pmatrix} 3 & 2 \\ 5 & 3 \end{pmatrix}$ which have the same number of rows as columns are known as *square matrices*.

Equality of matrices

Two matrices are equal if and only if they have the same order, and each element in one matrix is equal to the corresponding element in the other matrix. If, for example,

$$\mathbf{A} = \begin{pmatrix} 1 & 3 \\ 2 & 4 \end{pmatrix} \qquad \mathbf{B} = \begin{pmatrix} 1 & 2 \\ 3 & 4 \end{pmatrix} \qquad \mathbf{C} = \begin{pmatrix} 1 & 3 & 0 \\ 2 & 4 & 0 \end{pmatrix} \qquad \mathbf{D} = \begin{pmatrix} 1 & 3 \\ 2 & 4 \end{pmatrix}$$

the three matrices **A**, **B**, **C** are not equal to each other, but **A** and **D** are.

Addition and subtraction of matrices

Matrices of the *same order* may be added or subtracted element by element:

$$\begin{pmatrix} 1 & 3 \\ 2 & 4 \end{pmatrix} + \begin{pmatrix} 5 & 0 \\ -2 & 7 \end{pmatrix} = \begin{pmatrix} 6 & 3 \\ 0 & 11 \end{pmatrix}$$

$$\begin{pmatrix} 1 & 4 \\ 2 & 5 \\ 3 & 6 \end{pmatrix} - \begin{pmatrix} 4 & -2 \\ -3 & 7 \\ 5 & 6 \end{pmatrix} = \begin{pmatrix} -3 & 6 \\ 5 & -2 \\ -2 & 0 \end{pmatrix}.$$

But $\begin{pmatrix} 1 & 3 \\ 2 & 4 \end{pmatrix} + \begin{pmatrix} 1 \\ 0 \end{pmatrix}$ cannot be evaluated because the matrices are not of the same order. They are incompatible, or do not conform.

The matrix $\mathbf{O} = \begin{pmatrix} 0 & 0 \\ 0 & 0 \end{pmatrix}$ is known as the 2×2 *zero matrix*.

ACTIVITY

Explain why matrix addition is:

(i) commutative, i.e. **A** + **B** = **B** + **A**;

(ii) associative, i.e. **A** + (**B** + **C**) = (**A** + **B**) + **C**.

Multiplying a matrix by a number

You multiply a matrix by a number by multiplying each element by that number:

$$3 \times \begin{pmatrix} 1 & 3 \\ 2 & 4 \end{pmatrix} = \begin{pmatrix} 3 & 9 \\ 6 & 12 \end{pmatrix}.$$

Multiplication of matrices

At first sight matrix multiplication looks complicated and artificial. But with practice you will find it straightforward. There are good reasons for these strange routines as you will see on page 100!

The transformation defined by the matrix $\mathbf{M} = \begin{pmatrix} 2 & 5 \\ 4 & 3 \end{pmatrix}$ maps the point P with position vector $\mathbf{p} = \begin{pmatrix} x \\ y \end{pmatrix}$ to the point P′ with position vector $\mathbf{p}' = \begin{pmatrix} x' \\ y' \end{pmatrix}$ where

$$\begin{cases} x' = 2x + 5y \\ y' = 4x + 3y \end{cases}$$

So you can write

$$\mathbf{p}' = \begin{pmatrix} 2x + 5y \\ 4x + 3y \end{pmatrix}.$$

The 2×1 matrix $\mathbf{p}'$ above is an example of a matrix product; it is the product of the 2×2 matrix $\mathbf{M}$ with the 2×1 matrix $\mathbf{p}$, *in that order*:

$$\begin{pmatrix} 2 & 5 \\ 4 & 3 \end{pmatrix}\begin{pmatrix} x \\ y \end{pmatrix} = \begin{pmatrix} 2x + 5y \\ 4x + 3y \end{pmatrix}.$$

EXAMPLE 5.3

Calculate $\begin{pmatrix} 1 & 6 \\ 3 & 4 \end{pmatrix}\begin{pmatrix} 5 \\ 8 \end{pmatrix}$.

SOLUTION

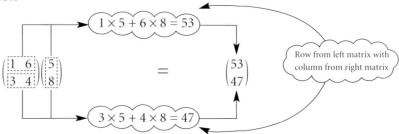

Figure 5.11

ACTIVITY

Figure 5.12 shows flag ABCD and its image A′B′C′D′ after applying the rotation matrix $\begin{pmatrix} 0.8 & -0.6 \\ 0.6 & 0.8 \end{pmatrix}$.

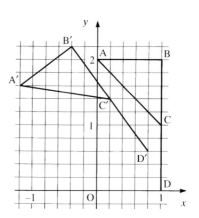

Figure 5.12

By calculating $\begin{pmatrix} 0.8 & -0.6 \\ 0.6 & 0.8 \end{pmatrix}\begin{pmatrix} 0 \\ 2 \end{pmatrix}$, $\begin{pmatrix} 0.8 & -0.6 \\ 0.6 & 0.8 \end{pmatrix}\begin{pmatrix} 1 \\ 2 \end{pmatrix}$ and two other matrix products, check that A′, B′, C′ and D′ have been plotted correctly.

A similar technique applies to all matrix multiplications. You use each row of the first (i.e. left) matrix with each column, in turn, of the second matrix. Figure 5.13 shows the steps used when multiplying a 2×2 matrix by a 2×3 matrix. The product is another 2×3 matrix.

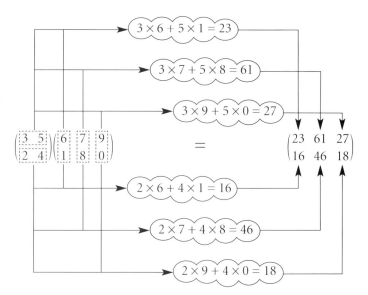

Figure 5.13

The four matrix multiplications of the last activity can be combined into one matrix multiplication:

$$\begin{pmatrix} 0.8 & -0.6 \\ 0.6 & 0.8 \end{pmatrix}\begin{pmatrix} 0 & 1 & 1 & 1 \\ 2 & 2 & 1 & 0 \end{pmatrix} = \begin{pmatrix} -1.2 & -0.4 & 0.2 & 0.8 \\ 1.6 & 2.2 & 1.4 & 0.6 \end{pmatrix}.$$

If you multiply a 3×4 matrix (on the left) by a 4×2 matrix (on the right) similar rules apply; the product is a 3×2 matrix. For example:

$$\begin{pmatrix} 1 & 2 & 4 & 7 \\ -3 & 5 & 0 & 1 \\ 4 & 2 & 3 & 5 \end{pmatrix}\begin{pmatrix} 5 & 1 \\ -6 & 4 \\ 8 & 9 \\ 2 & 2 \end{pmatrix} = \begin{pmatrix} 39 & 59 \\ -43 & 19 \\ 42 & 49 \end{pmatrix}.$$

Properties of matrix multiplication

MATRICES MUST BE CONFORMABLE FOR MULTIPLICATION

To be able to multiply two matrices together the number of columns in the first (left) matrix must equal the number of rows in the second matrix. If the first matrix is 3×4, the second must be $4 \times$ something. You say that the matrices need to *conform*. Generally, if **M** is $p \times q$, and **N** is $q \times r$, the product **MN** exists and is of order $p \times r$. It may be helpful to think of the rules for joining dominoes end to end.

$$\boxed{p \times q} \quad \boxed{q \times r} \quad \text{gives} \quad \boxed{p \times r}$$

MATRIX MULTIPLICATION IS NOT COMMUTATIVE

If $\mathbf{A} = \begin{pmatrix} 3 & 1 \\ 2 & 7 \end{pmatrix}$ and $\mathbf{B} = \begin{pmatrix} 4 & -2 \\ 1 & 5 \end{pmatrix}$ the product **AB** is given by

$$\mathbf{AB} = \begin{pmatrix} 3 & 1 \\ 2 & 7 \end{pmatrix}\begin{pmatrix} 4 & -2 \\ 1 & 5 \end{pmatrix} = \begin{pmatrix} 13 & -1 \\ 15 & 31 \end{pmatrix}$$

and the product **BA** by

$$\mathbf{BA} = \begin{pmatrix} 4 & -2 \\ 1 & 5 \end{pmatrix}\begin{pmatrix} 3 & 1 \\ 2 & 7 \end{pmatrix} = \begin{pmatrix} 8 & -10 \\ 13 & 36 \end{pmatrix}.$$

As $\mathbf{AB} \neq \mathbf{BA}$, matrix multiplication is not commutative. It matters which way round you write your matrices. Indeed, sometimes the product **MN** exists but the product **NM** does not exist, because the number of columns in **N** does not match the number of rows in **M**. For example if

$$\mathbf{M} = \begin{pmatrix} 2 & -4 \\ 5 & 3 \end{pmatrix} \quad \text{and} \quad \mathbf{N} = \begin{pmatrix} 6 & -2 & 7 \\ 4 & 3 & -5 \end{pmatrix}$$

then

$$\mathbf{MN} = \begin{pmatrix} 2 & -4 \\ 5 & 3 \end{pmatrix}\begin{pmatrix} 6 & -2 & 7 \\ 4 & 3 & -5 \end{pmatrix} = \begin{pmatrix} -4 & -16 & 34 \\ 42 & -1 & 20 \end{pmatrix};$$

but the product $\mathbf{NM} = \begin{pmatrix} 6 & -2 & 7 \\ 4 & 3 & -5 \end{pmatrix}\begin{pmatrix} 2 & -4 \\ 5 & 3 \end{pmatrix}$ is not defined.

MATRIX MULTIPLICATION IS ASSOCIATIVE

Whenever matrices **P, Q, R** are conformable for multiplication, $(\mathbf{PQ})\mathbf{R} = \mathbf{P}(\mathbf{QR})$. This is the associative property of matrix multiplication: the proof of this is shown on page 100.

ACTIVITY

Using $\mathbf{P} = \begin{pmatrix} 2 & 4 \\ -3 & 1 \end{pmatrix}$, $\mathbf{Q} = \begin{pmatrix} 5 & -3 \\ 1 & 2 \end{pmatrix}$ and $\mathbf{R} = \begin{pmatrix} 4 & -3 \\ 2 & 1 \end{pmatrix}$ calculate

(i) PQ   **(ii)** (PQ)R   **(iii)** QR   **(iv)** P(QR)

and so demonstrate the associative property of matrix multiplication.

MATRIX MULTIPLICATION IS DISTRIBUTIVE OVER MATRIX ADDITION

Provided the matrices **P, Q, R** conform so that the sums and products exist,

$$\mathbf{P}(\mathbf{Q} + \mathbf{R}) = \mathbf{PQ} + \mathbf{PR}.$$

It may also be proved that

$$(\mathbf{P} + \mathbf{Q})\mathbf{R} = \mathbf{PR} + \mathbf{QR}.$$

These two properties are what we mean when we say that matrix multiplication is distributive over matrix addition.

 1 Choose any three 2×2 matrices **P, Q, R** and check by direct evaluation that
P(Q + R) = PQ + PR.

2 By considering the elements in corresponding columns of the three matrices
B, C and **B + C**, show that **A(B + C) = AB + AC**.

The identity matrix

Whenever you multiply a 2×2 matrix **M** by $\mathbf{I} = \begin{pmatrix} 1 & 0 \\ 0 & 1 \end{pmatrix}$ the product is **M**.

It makes no difference whether you pre-multiply by **I**, as in

$$\begin{pmatrix} 1 & 0 \\ 0 & 1 \end{pmatrix}\begin{pmatrix} 3 & 5 \\ 7 & -2 \end{pmatrix} = \begin{pmatrix} 3 & 5 \\ 7 & -2 \end{pmatrix}$$

or post-multiply by **I**, as in

$$\begin{pmatrix} a & c \\ b & d \end{pmatrix}\begin{pmatrix} 1 & 0 \\ 0 & 1 \end{pmatrix} = \begin{pmatrix} a & c \\ b & d \end{pmatrix}.$$

For multiplication of 2×2 matrices, **I** behaves in the same way as the number 1 when dealing with multiplication of real numbers. **I** is known as the 2×2 *identity matrix*.

The 3×3 identity matrix (which we shall denote by $\mathbf{I}_3$) is $\begin{pmatrix} 1 & 0 & 0 \\ 0 & 1 & 0 \\ 0 & 0 & 1 \end{pmatrix}$.

| ACTIVITY

Show that $\mathbf{I}_3\mathbf{M} = \mathbf{M}$ and $\mathbf{M}\mathbf{I}_3 = \mathbf{M}$ for any 3×3 matrix you like to choose.

 Why is there no such thing as a 2×3 identity matrix?

Inverse matrices

Let $\mathbf{A} = \begin{pmatrix} 4 & 2 \\ 5 & 3 \end{pmatrix}$ and $\mathbf{B} = \begin{pmatrix} 3 & -2 \\ -5 & 4 \end{pmatrix}$. Then $\mathbf{AB} = \begin{pmatrix} 4 & 2 \\ 5 & 3 \end{pmatrix}\begin{pmatrix} 3 & -2 \\ -5 & 4 \end{pmatrix} = \begin{pmatrix} 2 & 0 \\ 0 & 2 \end{pmatrix}$.

Therefore the product of **A** and $\frac{1}{2}\mathbf{B}$ is $\begin{pmatrix} 1 & 0 \\ 0 & 1 \end{pmatrix}$.

If the product of two square matrices, **M** and **N**, is the identity matrix, **N** is known as the *inverse* of **M**. We write $\mathbf{N} = \mathbf{M}^{-1}$.

ACTIVITY

Suppose $\mathbf{M}^{-1} = \begin{pmatrix} w & y \\ x & z \end{pmatrix}$ where $\mathbf{M} = \begin{pmatrix} a & c \\ b & d \end{pmatrix}$. Multiply these two matrices together, equate the result to $\begin{pmatrix} 1 & 0 \\ 0 & 1 \end{pmatrix}$ and so form two pairs of equations.

Solve these as pairs of simultaneous equations, to show that $\mathbf{M}^{-1} = \dfrac{1}{\Delta}\begin{pmatrix} d & -c \\ -b & a \end{pmatrix}$, where $\Delta = ad - bc$, provided $\Delta \neq 0$.

The number $ad - bc$ is known as the *determinant* of the 2×2 matrix. If the determinant is 0, the matrix $\begin{pmatrix} a & c \\ b & d \end{pmatrix}$ does not have an inverse and is described as *singular*.

EXAMPLE 5.4

Find the inverses of the matrices **(i)** $\begin{pmatrix} 7 & 8 \\ 3 & 4 \end{pmatrix}$ and **(ii)** $\begin{pmatrix} 2 & 8 \\ 1 & 4 \end{pmatrix}$.

SOLUTION

(i) $\begin{pmatrix} 7 & 8 \\ 3 & 4 \end{pmatrix} = \dfrac{1}{4}\begin{pmatrix} 4 & -8 \\ -3 & 7 \end{pmatrix}$ which may be written as $\begin{pmatrix} 1 & -2 \\ -\frac{3}{4} & \frac{7}{4} \end{pmatrix}$.

$7 \times 4 - 3 \times 8 = 4$

Interchange the elements on the leading diagonal (from top left to bottom right) and change the sign of the two other elements

(ii) The determinant of $\begin{pmatrix} 2 & 8 \\ 1 & 4 \end{pmatrix}$ is $2 \times 4 - 1 \times 8 = 0$, so $\begin{pmatrix} 2 & 8 \\ 1 & 4 \end{pmatrix}$ has no inverse.

As matrix multiplication is not commutative, you may have been wondering if it matters in which order you multiply the two matrices in the last activity. In Example 5.5 we prove that it does not matter whether you pre-multiply $\mathbf{M}$ by $\mathbf{M}^{-1}$ (forming $\mathbf{M}^{-1}\mathbf{M}$) or post-multiply $\mathbf{M}$ by $\mathbf{M}^{-1}$ (forming $\mathbf{M}\mathbf{M}^{-1}$): the product is $\mathbf{I}$, the identity matrix.

EXAMPLE 5.5

$\mathbf{M}$ is a square matrix, and $\mathbf{L}$ and $\mathbf{R}$ are matrices such that $\mathbf{L}\mathbf{M} = \mathbf{I}$ and $\mathbf{M}\mathbf{R} = \mathbf{I}$. Prove that $\mathbf{L} = \mathbf{R}$.

SOLUTION

$\mathbf{L}\mathbf{M} = \mathbf{I}$

$\Rightarrow (\mathbf{L}\mathbf{M})\mathbf{R} = \mathbf{I}\mathbf{R}$ — Post-multiplying both sides by $\mathbf{R}$

$\Rightarrow \mathbf{L}(\mathbf{M}\mathbf{R}) = \mathbf{R}$ — Matrix multiplication is associative

$\Rightarrow \mathbf{L}\mathbf{I} = \mathbf{R}$

$\Rightarrow \mathbf{L} = \mathbf{R}$

This is an important result: it means that the inverse of a matrix (if it exists) is unique. This applies to all (square) matrices, not just 2×2 matrices.

If the determinant of a square matrix is not 0 the inverse of the matrix exists, and the matrix is described as *non-singular*. The determinant of a *singular* matrix is 0.

In the Appendix (page 153) you will see how to find the determinant of a 3×3 matrix, but further work on the inverses of 3×3 matrices is left to *Pure Mathematics 6*.

ACTIVITY

If your calculator handles matrices find out how you should input them. Particularly notice whether the calculator encourages you to input by rows or by columns. Find out how to add and multiply matrices on your calculator, and how to find the inverse of a matrix.

Historical note

The multiplication of matrices was first fully defined by Arthur Cayley (1821–95) in 1858. Cayley's mathematical talent was noticed while he was at school (in London), and his first mathematical paper was published in 1841, while he was an undergraduate at Cambridge. He worked as a lawyer for some 14 years, refusing more cases than he accepted as he only wanted to earn sufficient to enable him to get on with 'his work'; during this period he published nearly 200 mathematical papers. In 1863 he returned to Cambridge as a professor. As well as his work on matrices, he developed the geometry of n-dimensional spaces and is known for his work on the theory of invariants, much of this in collaboration with his life-long friend, James Joseph Sylvester (1814–97). It was Sylvester who, in 1850, coined the word 'matrix', Latin for 'womb'; in geology a matrix is a mass of rock enclosing gems; so in mathematics a matrix is a container of (valuable) information. It was at about this time that Florence Nightingale was one of Sylvester's pupils.

EXERCISE 5B

In Questions 1–4 *use*:

$$A = \begin{pmatrix} 3 & 1 \\ 2 & 4 \end{pmatrix} \qquad B = \begin{pmatrix} -3 & 7 \\ 2 & 5 \end{pmatrix} \qquad C = \begin{pmatrix} 2 & 3 & 4 \\ 5 & 7 & 1 \end{pmatrix}$$

$$D = \begin{pmatrix} 3 & 4 \\ 7 & 0 \\ 1 & -2 \end{pmatrix} \qquad E = \begin{pmatrix} 4 & 7 \\ 3 & -2 \\ 1 & 5 \end{pmatrix} \qquad F = \begin{pmatrix} 3 & 7 & -5 \\ 2 & 6 & 0 \\ -1 & 4 & 8 \end{pmatrix}$$

1 Calculate (if possible)

(i) $\quad$ A + B	**(ii)** $\quad$ 3C	**(iii)** $\quad$ B + C
(iv) $\quad$ C − D	**(v)** $\quad$ D − E	**(vi)** $\quad$ AB
(vii) CA	**(viii)** BC	**(ix)** $\quad$ CD
(x) $\quad$ DC	**(xi)** $\quad$ AF	**(xii)** BE
(xiii) 4F + EC	**(xiv)** EA	**(xv)** FE

2 By calculating (if possible) **AB**, **BA**, **AD** and **DA** demonstrate that matrix multiplication is not commutative.

3 Demonstrate the associative property of matrix multiplication by calculating both (**AC**)**F** and **A**(**CF**).

4 Calculate **(i)** $\mathbf{A}^{-1}$ **(ii)** $\mathbf{B}^{-1}$ **(iii)** $\mathbf{AB}$ **(iv)** $(\mathbf{AB})^{-1}$.
Is $(\mathbf{AB})^{-1}$ the same as $\mathbf{A}^{-1}\mathbf{B}^{-1}$ or the same as $\mathbf{B}^{-1}\mathbf{A}^{-1}$?

5 Where possible find the inverses of the following matrices.

(i) $\begin{pmatrix} 4 & 3 \\ 6 & 5 \end{pmatrix}$ 　　**(ii)** $\begin{pmatrix} 6 & -3 \\ -4 & -2 \end{pmatrix}$ 　　**(iii)** $\begin{pmatrix} 5 & 6 \\ 2 & 3 \end{pmatrix}$

(iv) $\begin{pmatrix} \frac{1}{3} & \frac{3}{4} \\ \frac{2}{3} & 2 \end{pmatrix}$ 　　**(v)** $\begin{pmatrix} e & f \\ g & h \end{pmatrix}$

6 The matrix $\begin{pmatrix} 1-k & 2 \\ -1 & 4-k \end{pmatrix}$ is singular. Find the possible values of k.

7 The diagram shows a flag.

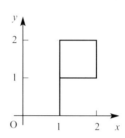

(i) Use the matrix $\begin{pmatrix} -0.6 & 0.8 \\ 0.8 & 0.6 \end{pmatrix}$ to transform the flag, and draw the original flag and its image on one diagram.

(ii) Describe the transformation in words.

8 Triangle T has its vertices at $(1, 0)$, $(0, 1)$ and $(-2, 0)$. It is transformed to triangle T′ by means of the matrix $\mathbf{M} = \begin{pmatrix} 3 & 1 \\ 1 & 1 \end{pmatrix}$.

(i) Find the co-ordinates of the vertices of T′, and show T and T′ on one diagram.

(ii) Find the ratio of the area of T′ to the area of T, and the value of the determinant of $\mathbf{M}$.

9 (i) Choose a shape of your own. Call it S.

(ii) Transform S using the matrix $\mathbf{M} = \begin{pmatrix} 2 & 1 \\ 1 & -2 \end{pmatrix}$ to form the image S′. Draw S′.

(iii) Calculate $\mathbf{M}^2$.

(iv) Describe as simply as you can the single transformation represented by $\mathbf{M}^2$.

10 $\mathbf{A} = \begin{pmatrix} 5 & 3 \\ 6 & 4 \end{pmatrix}$　$\mathbf{B} = \begin{pmatrix} 4 & 3 \\ 1 & 2 \end{pmatrix}$. Calculate

(i) $\mathbf{A}^{-1}$ 　　　　**(ii)** $\mathbf{B}^{-1}$ 　　　　**(iii)** $\mathbf{A}^{-1}\mathbf{B}^{-1}$

(iv) $\mathbf{B}^{-1}\mathbf{A}^{-1}$ 　　**(v)** $(\mathbf{BA})^{-1}$ 　　**(vi)** $(\mathbf{AB})^{-1}$

Comment on your results.

11 A 2×2 singular matrix $\mathbf{M}$ is given as $\begin{pmatrix} a & c \\ b & d \end{pmatrix}$.

Find $\mathbf{M}^2$ and give your answer as a multiple of $\mathbf{M}$.

Hence find a formula which gives $\mathbf{M}^n$ in terms of $\mathbf{M}$.

[MEI, part]

12 The matrix $\mathbf{S} = \begin{pmatrix} 5 & 0 & 1 & 6 & 2 \\ 7 & 8 & 4 & 3 & 9 \end{pmatrix}$ contains the numbers of first and second class stamps used in an office each day last week. (Top row denotes first class.)

  (i) Find a matrix $\mathbf{D}$ such that $\mathbf{DS}$ gives the total number of stamps used each day.
  (ii) Find a matrix $\mathbf{N}$ such that $\mathbf{SN}$ gives the total number of each type of stamp used in the week.
  (iii) First class stamps cost 27 pence while second class stamps cost 19 pence. Find a way of calculating the total cost of last week′s stamps using only matrix multiplication.

13 The stylised map below shows the bus routes in a holiday area. Lines represent routes that run each way between the resorts. Arrows indicate one-way scenic routes. $\mathbf{M}$ is the partly completed 4×4 matrix which shows the number of direct routes between the various resorts. Copy and complete $\mathbf{M}$. Calculate $\mathbf{M}^2$ and explain what information it contains. What information would $\mathbf{M}^3$ contain?

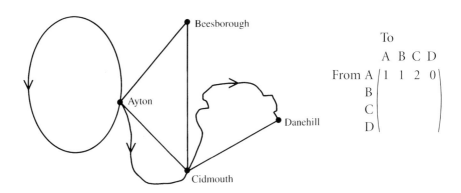

$$\text{To}$$
$$\begin{array}{cccc} & A & B & C & D \end{array}$$
$$\text{From} \begin{array}{c} A \\ B \\ C \\ D \end{array} \begin{pmatrix} 1 & 1 & 2 & 0 \\ & & & \\ & & & \\ & & & \end{pmatrix}$$

14 The figure shows the start of the plaiting process, using three strands, a, b and c.

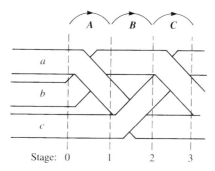

The process has only two steps, repeated alternately:
A: cross the top strand *over* the middle strand;
B: cross the middle strand *under* the bottom strand.

At Stage 0 the order of the strands is given by $\mathbf{s}_0 = \begin{pmatrix} a \\ b \\ c \end{pmatrix}$.

(i) Show that pre-multiplying s_0 by the matrix $\mathbf{A} = \begin{pmatrix} 0 & 1 & 0 \\ 1 & 0 & 0 \\ 0 & 0 & 1 \end{pmatrix}$ gives s_1, the vector which represents the order of the strands at Stage 1.

(ii) Find the 3×3 matrix $\mathbf{B}$ which represents the transition from Stage 1 to Stage 2.

(iii) Find matrix $\mathbf{M} = \mathbf{BA}$ and show that $\mathbf{M}s_0$ gives s_2, the vector which represents the order of the strands at Stage 2.

(iv) Find $\mathbf{M}^2$ and hence find the order of the strands at Stage 4.

(v) Calculate $\mathbf{M}^3$. What does this tell you?

15 There are two basic types of four-terminal electrical network (see the diagram).

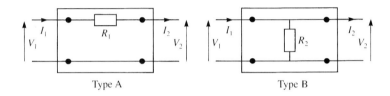

Type A   Type B

(i) In Type A the output voltage V_2 and current I_2 are related to the input voltage V_1 and current I_1 by the simultaneous equations

$$V_2 = V_1 - I_1 R_1$$
$$I_2 = I_1$$

We may write $\begin{pmatrix} V_2 \\ I_2 \end{pmatrix} = \mathbf{A} \begin{pmatrix} V_1 \\ I_1 \end{pmatrix}$. Write down matrix $\mathbf{A}$.

(ii) In Type B the corresponding simultaneous equations are

$$V_2 = V_1$$
$$I_2 = I_1 - \frac{V_1}{R_2}$$

Write down the matrix $\mathbf{B}$ which represents the effect of a Type B network.

(iii) Find the matrix which represents the effect of Type A followed by Type B.

(iv) Is the effect of Type B followed by Type A the same as the effect of Type A followed by Type B?

Properties of transformations

Notation

A single letter, such as T, is often used to represent a transformation. Then the image of the point P may be denoted by $T(P)$ or by P′. The point P has position vector $\mathbf{p}$; its image $T(P)$ has position vector $\mathbf{p}' = T(\mathbf{p})$. We find $T(\mathbf{p})$ by evaluating the matrix product $\mathbf{Tp}$, where $\mathbf{T}$ is the matrix which represents T. Notice that bold italic T is used for the transformation and bold upright $\mathbf{T}$ for the matrix.

Composition of transformations

If you use X to represent reflection in the x axis, then X maps the point P to the point $X(P)$, figure 5.14.

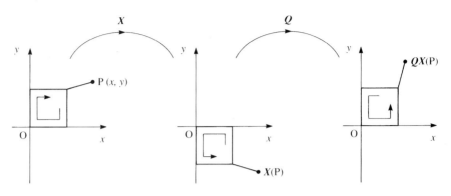

Figure 5.14

If Q represents a quarter turn anticlockwise about O, and you apply Q to the image formed by X, the point $X(P)$ is mapped to $Q(X(P))$. This is abbreviated to $QX(P)$. The composite transformation:

> reflection in the x axis followed by a quarter turn anticlockwise about O

is represented by QX. Note the order. From figure 5.14 you will recognise that QX is equivalent to reflection in the line $y = x$.

Reflection X is represented by the matrix $X = \begin{pmatrix} 1 & 0 \\ 0 & -1 \end{pmatrix}$; the quarter turn Q is represented by $Q = \begin{pmatrix} 0 & -1 \\ 1 & 0 \end{pmatrix}$. Direct calculation will confirm that the product QX is $\begin{pmatrix} 0 & 1 \\ 1 & 0 \end{pmatrix}$, the matrix which represents reflection in the line $y = x$.

Again notice the order in which the matrices were arranged for the multiplication: the matrix representing the first transformation is on the right, and the matrix for the second transformation is on the left.

More generally, the matrix of this form of composite transformation is found by multiplying the matrices of the component transformations, in the correct order. To prove this suppose that the transformations T and S are represented by the matrices $T = \begin{pmatrix} a & c \\ b & d \end{pmatrix}$ and $S = \begin{pmatrix} p & r \\ q & s \end{pmatrix}$ respectively. Applying T to the point P with position vector $\begin{pmatrix} x \\ y \end{pmatrix}$ we obtain P′ with position vector $\begin{pmatrix} x' \\ y' \end{pmatrix} = \begin{pmatrix} ax + cy \\ bx + dy \end{pmatrix}$. Then applying S to P′ gives P″, with position vector $\begin{pmatrix} x'' \\ y'' \end{pmatrix}$, as shown in figure 5.15.

Use U to represent the composite transformation ST, T followed by S.

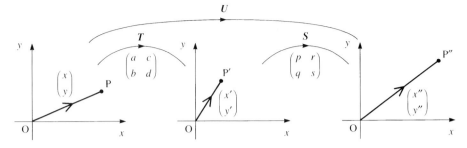

Figure 5.15

Then $\quad x'' = px' + ry'$

$\qquad\qquad = p(ax + cy) + r(bx + dy) \quad$ since $x' = ax + cy$ and $y' = bx + dy$

$\qquad\qquad = (pa + rb)x + (pc + rd)y.$

Similarly $\quad y'' = (qa + sb)x + (qc + sd)y.$

Thus the matrix for the composite transformation $U = ST$ is

$$\begin{pmatrix} pa + rb & pc + rd \\ qa + sb & qc + sd \end{pmatrix}$$

which is what you have already defined as the matrix product $\begin{pmatrix} p & r \\ q & s \end{pmatrix}\begin{pmatrix} a & c \\ b & d \end{pmatrix}$.

Proof that matrix multiplication is associative

You can extend this to combine three or more transformations. If *L*, *M* and *N* are three transformations, then *L*(*MN*) represents the composite transformation

> do *N* first, then do *M* to the resulting figure, and finally do *L* to the image made by *M*.

If the corresponding matrices are **L**, **M** and **N** then the matrix representing *L*(*MN*) is the product **L**(**MN**). In essence, the matrix **L**(**MN**) represents the instructions:

> apply *N* and then *M*, pause, and then apply *L*.

Similarly the matrix (**LM**)**N** represents the instructions:

> apply *N*, pause, and then apply *M* and then *L*.

Where you pause makes no difference!

As both matrix products **L**(**MN**) and (**LM**)**N** represent the same sequence of transformations, applied in the same order, producing the same result, they represent the same composite transformation. You can conclude that matrix multiplication is associative. It does not matter whether you calculate **L**(**MN**) or (**LM**)**N**; the brackets are superfluous, and are usually omitted.

What difference (if any) does it make to the above reasoning if

(i) the order of matrices **L**, **M** and **N** is 3×3;

(ii) the matrices **L**, **M** and **N** are not square;

(iii) the order of the matrices is 4×4?

Inverses

You can again use **Q** to represent a quarter turn anticlockwise about O; the corresponding matrix is $\mathbf{Q} = \begin{pmatrix} 0 & -1 \\ 1 & 0 \end{pmatrix}$. Check that det **Q** = 1, and that $\mathbf{Q}^{-1} = \begin{pmatrix} 0 & 1 \\ -1 & 0 \end{pmatrix}$. You will recognise $\mathbf{Q}^{-1}$ as the matrix which represents a quarter turn clockwise about O, the transformation which undoes the effect of **Q**. It is known as the inverse of **Q**, and is denoted by $\mathbf{Q}^{-1}$. This is typical of the general pattern: if T is a transformation with matrix **T**, the *inverse* of T (if it exists) is the transformation denoted by T^{-1} which undoes the effect of T; T^{-1} has matrix $\mathbf{T}^{-1}$.

Now suppose you want to find the inverse of the product **AB**, where **A** and **B** are non-singular matrices, i.e. you want to find **X** such that $\mathbf{X(AB)} = \mathbf{I}$. Repeatedly using the fact that matrix multiplication is associative you have

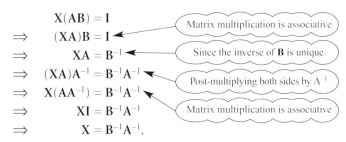

$$\mathbf{X(AB)} = \mathbf{I}$$
$$\Rightarrow \quad \mathbf{(XA)B} = \mathbf{I}$$
$$\Rightarrow \quad \mathbf{XA} = \mathbf{B}^{-1}$$
$$\Rightarrow \quad \mathbf{(XA)A}^{-1} = \mathbf{B}^{-1}\mathbf{A}^{-1}$$
$$\Rightarrow \quad \mathbf{X(AA}^{-1}) = \mathbf{B}^{-1}\mathbf{A}^{-1}$$
$$\Rightarrow \quad \mathbf{XI} = \mathbf{B}^{-1}\mathbf{A}^{-1}$$
$$\Rightarrow \quad \mathbf{X} = \mathbf{B}^{-1}\mathbf{A}^{-1}.$$

(Matrix multiplication is associative)
(Since the inverse of **B** is unique)
(Post-multiplying both sides by $\mathbf{A}^{-1}$)
(Matrix multiplication is associative)

Thus $\mathbf{(AB)}^{-1} = \mathbf{B}^{-1}\mathbf{A}^{-1}$, where **A** and **B** are non-singular matrices of the same order. You put your socks on before your shoes, but presumably you take your shoes off before your socks!

ACTIVITY

As often happens, it is easier when you know the answer! Use the associative property of matrix multiplication to show that $\mathbf{(AB)(B}^{-1}\mathbf{A}^{-1})$ simplifies to **I** and so provide an alternative proof that $\mathbf{(AB)}^{-1} = \mathbf{B}^{-1}\mathbf{A}^{-1}$.

EXERCISE 5C

1 X represents reflection in the x axis and J represents a quarter turn clockwise about the origin. Write down the matrices which represent X and J.

(i) Find the matrix which represents JX. Describe the transformation JX as simply as you can.

(ii) Repeat part (i) for the transformation XJ.

2 Transformations **R** and **S** are represented by matrices $\mathbf{R} = \begin{pmatrix} 2 & -1 \\ 1 & 3 \end{pmatrix}$ and $\mathbf{S} = \begin{pmatrix} 3 & 0 \\ -2 & 4 \end{pmatrix}$. Find the matrix which represents the transformation **RS**.

3 Write down the matrix **M** which represents reflection of the plane in the line $y = x \tan \theta$. Show that $\mathbf{M}^{-1} = \mathbf{M}$, and verify that $\mathbf{M}^2 = \mathbf{I}$.

4 Write down the matrix **R** which represents rotation of the plane through angle α anticlockwise about the origin. Explain why it should be possible to obtain $\mathbf{R}^{-1}$ from **R** by replacing α by $-\alpha$. Verify that this is so.

5 Prove that $(\mathbf{PQ})^{-1} = \mathbf{Q}^{-1}\mathbf{P}^{-1}$ and verify the formula by direct calculation in the case $\mathbf{P} = \begin{pmatrix} 2 & 3 \\ 2 & 4 \end{pmatrix}$ and $\mathbf{Q} = \begin{pmatrix} 4 & 3 \\ 5 & 5 \end{pmatrix}$.

6 R_α and R_β represent rotation of the plane through angles α and β anticlockwise about the origin. The corresponding matrices are $\mathbf{R}_\alpha$ and $\mathbf{R}_\beta$.

(i) By considering the effects of the rotations, explain why $R_\alpha R_\beta = R_\beta R_\alpha$.
(ii) Write down $\mathbf{R}_\alpha$ and $\mathbf{R}_\beta$ and calculate $\mathbf{R}_\alpha \mathbf{R}_\beta$, simplifying your answer as much as possible.
(iii) Describe as simply as possible a single transformation equivalent to $R_\alpha R_\beta$.

7 (i) Write down the matrix **R** which represents the rotation through 30° anticlockwise about the origin and the matrix **M** which represents reflection in the line $y = \sqrt{3}x$.
(ii) Calculate **MR**. What single transformation does this matrix represent?
(iii) What single transformation does the matrix **RM** represent?

8 A shear **S** maps $(1, 0)$ to $(2, 3)$ and leaves the origin at the origin. Find the matrix **M** which represents **S** and verify that $\mathbf{M}^{-1}$ represents the shear that maps $(2, 3)$ to $(1, 0)$ and leaves the origin at the origin.

9 (i) Write down the matrix which represents rotation through angle 2α about O.
(ii) Write down the matrix which represents reflection in the line $y = x \tan \theta$.
(iii) Use matrix multiplication to show that a rotation followed by a reflection in a line which passes through the centre of the rotation is equivalent to a single reflection.

10 Two mirror lines intersect at O. The angle between the mirrors is θ. Use matrix multiplication to prove that reflection in one line followed by reflection in the other line is equivalent to a rotation of 2θ about O.

11 A matrix **M** defines an anticlockwise rotation about the origin through an angle θ, mapping the point (x, y) to (x', y'), where

$$\begin{pmatrix} x' \\ y' \end{pmatrix} = \mathbf{M} \begin{pmatrix} x \\ y \end{pmatrix}.$$

(i) Show that $\mathbf{M} = \begin{pmatrix} \cos\theta & -\sin\theta \\ \sin\theta & \cos\theta \end{pmatrix}$.

(ii) Write down the matrix which corresponds to an anticlockwise rotation of 135° about the origin.

The lines $y = -4x$ and $y = 2x - 5\sqrt{2}$ are rotated anticlockwise through 135° about the origin.

(iii) Show that the image of the line $y = -4x$ is $y = \frac{5}{3}x$.

(iv) Find the equation of the image of the line $y = 2x - 5\sqrt{2}$.

[MEI]

12 (i) Two square matrices **M** and **N** (of the same size) have inverses $\mathbf{M}^{-1}$ and $\mathbf{N}^{-1}$ respectively. Show that the inverse of **MN** is $\mathbf{N}^{-1}\mathbf{M}^{-1}$.

(ii) $\mathbf{A} = \begin{pmatrix} 1 & 7 & 4 \\ 0 & 1 & 2 \\ 0 & 0 & 1 \end{pmatrix}$, $\mathbf{B} = \begin{pmatrix} 1 & 0 & 0 \\ 3 & 1 & 0 \\ -1 & -4 & 1 \end{pmatrix}$ and $\mathbf{C} = \mathbf{AB}$.

    (a) Evaluate the matrix **C**.

    (b) Work out the matrix product $\mathbf{A}\begin{pmatrix} 1 & a & b \\ 0 & 1 & c \\ 0 & 0 & 1 \end{pmatrix}$.

    (c) By equating the product in part **(b)** to $\begin{pmatrix} 1 & 0 & 0 \\ 0 & 1 & 0 \\ 0 & 0 & 1 \end{pmatrix}$, find $\mathbf{A}^{-1}$.

    (d) Using a similar method, or otherwise, find $\mathbf{B}^{-1}$.

    (e) Using your results from parts **(iii)** and **(iv)**, find $\mathbf{C}^{-1}$.

[MEI]

13 The one–way stretch **S**, ×5 parallel to the line $y = \frac{1}{2}x$ may be accomplished by

    (a) rotating the plane clockwise through the angle $\arctan\left(\frac{1}{2}\right)$ about O, and then

    (b) doing a one–way stretch, ×5 parallel to the x axis, and then

    (c) rotating the plane anticlockwise through the angle $\arctan\left(\frac{1}{2}\right)$ about O.

    (i) Find the matrix for each of the transformations described in **(a)**, **(b)** and **(c)**, and hence find the matrix which represents **S**.

    (ii) Transformation **S** maps figure F to F′. Describe the transformation which maps F′ to F and find its matrix.

14 The 2×2 matrix $\mathbf{Z} = \begin{pmatrix} a & c \\ b & d \end{pmatrix}$ is such that $\mathbf{Z}^2$ is the 2×2 zero matrix.

    (i) Show that **Z** can be expressed in terms of a and b only, or in terms of either b or c only.

    (ii) Show that when **Z** can be expressed in terms of b only, we can write $\mathbf{Z} = \mathbf{ERP}$, where

$$\mathbf{E} = \begin{pmatrix} b & 0 \\ 0 & b \end{pmatrix} \qquad \mathbf{R} = \begin{pmatrix} 0 & -1 \\ 1 & 0 \end{pmatrix} \qquad \mathbf{P} = \begin{pmatrix} 1 & 0 \\ 0 & 0 \end{pmatrix}.$$

    (iii) Describe the transformations represented by matrices **E**, **R** and **P**.

    (iv) Explain how this fits the fact that $\mathbf{Z}^2$ is the zero matrix.

15 You are given the matrix $\mathbf{A} = \begin{pmatrix} -1 & -4 \\ 1 & 3 \end{pmatrix}$.

  (i) Calculate $\mathbf{A}^2$ and $\mathbf{A}^3$.

  (ii) Show that the formula $\mathbf{A}^n = \begin{pmatrix} 1 - 2n & -4n \\ n & 1 + 2n \end{pmatrix}$ is consistent with the given

  value of $\mathbf{A}$ and your calculations for $n = 2$ and $n = 3$.

  (iii) Prove by induction that the formula for $\mathbf{A}^n$ is correct when n is a positive integer.

  (iv) Find the values of p and q for which

$$\mathbf{A}^2 = p\mathbf{A} + q\mathbf{I}.$$

  (v) Deduce that

$$\mathbf{A}^3 = p\mathbf{A}^2 + q\mathbf{A}.$$

  Using the result of part **(iv)** write this in the form

$$\mathbf{A}^3 = r\mathbf{A} + s\mathbf{I} \text{ and find } r \text{ and } s.$$

  (vi) Continue with this method to express $\mathbf{A}^4$ in terms of $\mathbf{A}$ and $\mathbf{I}$.

  (vii) Propose a formula for $\mathbf{A}^n$ in terms of $\mathbf{A}$ and $\mathbf{I}$ and show that it gives the same matrix $\mathbf{A}^n$ as you found in part **(ii)**.

[MEI]

Linear transformations

Many transformations have the property illustrated in Example 5.6.

EXAMPLE 5.6

Transformation T has matrix $\begin{pmatrix} 3 & 5 \\ 1 & 2 \end{pmatrix}$ and $\mathbf{p}$ and $\mathbf{q}$ are the vectors $\begin{pmatrix} x_1 \\ y_1 \end{pmatrix}$ and $\begin{pmatrix} x_2 \\ y_2 \end{pmatrix}$.

Find the image of the points with position vectors $\mathbf{p}$, $\mathbf{q}$, and $\lambda\mathbf{p} + \mu\mathbf{q}$, where λ and μ are arbitrary constants, and show that

$$T(\lambda\mathbf{p} + \mu\mathbf{q}) = \lambda T(\mathbf{p}) + \mu T(\mathbf{q}).$$

SOLUTION

$$T(\mathbf{p}) = \begin{pmatrix} 3 & 5 \\ 1 & 2 \end{pmatrix}\begin{pmatrix} x_1 \\ y_1 \end{pmatrix} = \begin{pmatrix} 3x_1 + 5y_1 \\ x_1 + 2y_1 \end{pmatrix}$$

$$T(\mathbf{q}) = \begin{pmatrix} 3 & 5 \\ 1 & 2 \end{pmatrix}\begin{pmatrix} x_2 \\ y_2 \end{pmatrix} = \begin{pmatrix} 3x_2 + 5y_2 \\ x_2 + 2y_2 \end{pmatrix}$$

$$T(\lambda\mathbf{p} + \mu\mathbf{q}) = \begin{pmatrix} 3 & 5 \\ 1 & 2 \end{pmatrix}\left(\lambda\begin{pmatrix} x_1 \\ y_1 \end{pmatrix} + \mu\begin{pmatrix} x_2 \\ y_2 \end{pmatrix}\right)$$

$$= \begin{pmatrix} 3(\lambda x_1 + \mu x_2) + 5(\lambda y_1 + \mu y_2) \\ (\lambda x_1 + \mu x_2) + 2(\lambda y_1 + \mu y_2) \end{pmatrix}$$

$$= \begin{pmatrix} \lambda(3x_1 + 5y_1) + \mu(3x_2 + 5y_2) \\ \lambda(x_1 + 2y_1) + \mu(x_2 + 2y_2) \end{pmatrix}$$

$$= \lambda\begin{pmatrix} 3x_1 + 5y_1 \\ x_1 + 2y_1 \end{pmatrix} + \mu\begin{pmatrix} 3x_2 + 5y_2 \\ x_2 + 2y_2 \end{pmatrix}$$

Thus $T(\lambda\mathbf{p} + \mu\mathbf{q}) = \lambda T(\mathbf{p}) + \mu T(\mathbf{q})$.

Any transformation *T* which has the property that

$$T(\lambda\mathbf{p} + \mu\mathbf{q}) = \lambda T(\mathbf{p}) + \mu T(\mathbf{q})$$

whatever the scalars λ and μ, and whatever the vectors $\mathbf{p}$ and $\mathbf{q}$, is known as a *linear transformation.*

Work exactly similar to that above shows that whenever you can specify a transformation *T* by means of a matrix **M**, so that the point P with position vector **p** maps to P′ with position vector $T(\mathbf{p}) = \mathbf{p}' = \mathbf{Mp}$, then

$$T(\lambda\mathbf{p} + \mu\mathbf{q}) = \lambda T(\mathbf{p}) + \mu T(\mathbf{q})$$

for all λ and μ, and for all **p** and **q**. This means that all transformations that can be represented in this way by matrices are linear transformations.

ACTIVITY

By writing **p** as **p** + **0** show that a linear transformation always maps the origin to the origin. Why is a non-zero translation not a linear transformation?

Perhaps surprisingly, if *T* is a linear transformation mapping **p** to **p′**, it can be represented by a matrix **M** in such a way that $\mathbf{p}' = \mathbf{Mp}$. The order of **M** depends on the dimensions of both the domain and the co-domain of *T*. Suppose, for example, *T* is a linear transformation mapping (x, y) to (x', y') in such a way that

$T(\mathbf{i}) = \begin{pmatrix} 3 \\ 2 \end{pmatrix}$ and $T(\mathbf{j}) = \begin{pmatrix} 0 \\ 4 \end{pmatrix}$. Then applying the definition of a linear transformation to *T* gives

$$\begin{aligned} T(x\mathbf{i} + y\mathbf{j}) &= xT(\mathbf{i}) + yT(\mathbf{j}) \\ &= x\begin{pmatrix} 3 \\ 2 \end{pmatrix} + y\begin{pmatrix} 0 \\ 4 \end{pmatrix} \\ &= \begin{pmatrix} 3x \\ 2x + 4y \end{pmatrix} \\ &= \mathbf{M}\begin{pmatrix} x \\ y \end{pmatrix} \quad \text{where } \mathbf{M} = \begin{pmatrix} 3 & 0 \\ 2 & 4 \end{pmatrix}. \end{aligned}$$

A similar proof applies in the general case.

Linear transformations preserve linearity

You will now prove that, under a linear transformation, the image of a line is a line. In other words, linear transformations preserve linearity.

Consider the line with equation $\mathbf{r} = \mathbf{a} + \lambda\mathbf{d}$. Then, under transformation *T*, the image of R is R′, with position vector

$$\begin{aligned} \mathbf{r}' = T(\mathbf{r}) &= T(\mathbf{a} + \lambda\mathbf{d}) \\ &= T(\mathbf{a}) + \lambda T(\mathbf{d}) \quad \text{since } T \text{ is a linear transformation.} \end{aligned}$$

Thus $\mathbf{r}' = \mathbf{a}' + \lambda\mathbf{d}'$, which is the equation of a straight line, provided (for the moment) that $\mathbf{d}' \neq \mathbf{0}$.

EXAMPLE 5.7

Find the image of the line *l* with equation $y = 2x + 3$ under the transformation *T* with matrix $\begin{pmatrix} 2 & 3 \\ 5 & 1 \end{pmatrix}$.

SOLUTION 1

As *T* is a linear transformation, it preserves linearity, so we can find the image of *l* by first finding the image of any two points on *l*.

A(0, 3) is on *l*. *T*(A) has position vector $\begin{pmatrix} 2 & 3 \\ 5 & 1 \end{pmatrix}\begin{pmatrix} 0 \\ 3 \end{pmatrix} = \begin{pmatrix} 9 \\ 3 \end{pmatrix}$.

B(2, 7) is on *l*. *T*(B) has position vector $\begin{pmatrix} 2 & 3 \\ 5 & 1 \end{pmatrix}\begin{pmatrix} 2 \\ 7 \end{pmatrix} = \begin{pmatrix} 25 \\ 17 \end{pmatrix}$.

The equation of the line passing through (9, 3) and (25, 17) is

$$y - 3 = \frac{17 - 3}{25 - 9}(x - 9)$$

$$\Rightarrow \quad y - 3 = \tfrac{7}{8}(x - 9)$$

$$\Rightarrow \quad 8y - 24 = 7x - 63$$

$$\Rightarrow \quad 7x - 8y = 39.$$

SOLUTION 2

The general point on the line $y = 2x + 3$ is $(t, 2t + 3)$. Its image (x', y') under *T* is given by

$$\begin{pmatrix} x' \\ y' \end{pmatrix} = \begin{pmatrix} 2 & 3 \\ 5 & 1 \end{pmatrix}\begin{pmatrix} t \\ 2t + 3 \end{pmatrix} = \begin{pmatrix} 8t + 9 \\ 7t + 3 \end{pmatrix}$$

Eliminating *t* from the equations

$$\begin{cases} x' = 8t + 9 \\ y' = 7t + 3 \end{cases}$$ gives $7x' - 8y' = 39$ so the image line has equation $7x - 8y = 39$.

EXERCISE 5D

1 Which of the following are linear transformations?
   (i) Reflection in $y = x$.
   (ii) Reflection in $y = x - 1$.
   (iii) Half turn about (2, 0).
   (iv) A positive quarter turn about (0, 0).
   (v) The shear with matrix $\begin{pmatrix} 1 & 2 \\ 0 & 1 \end{pmatrix}$.
   (vi) Enlargement, scale factor 2, centre (2, 1).

2 Transformation *T* is a projection. Each point is mapped on to *l*, the line $y = 2x$. The line joining each point to its image is perpendicular to *l*. Find the co-ordinates of the image of the point (p, q). Is *T* a linear transformation? Justify your decision.

3 Explain what is meant by the statement '*T* is a linear transformation'. If *T* maps (x, y) to $(|x|, y)$ is *T* a linear transformation? Use your definition to justify your answer.

4 A linear transformation maps distinct points A and B to A′ and B′. Show that

(i) A′ and B′ are distinct $\Rightarrow$ all points on line AB map to points on line A′B′;

(ii) A′ and B′ coincide $\Rightarrow$ all points on line AB map to A′.

5 Prove that under a linear transformation the images of parallel lines are parallel lines, and hence that the co-ordinate grid of unit squares maps into a grid of congruent parallelograms.

6 T is a linear transformation and the point C divides AB in the ratio $m : n$. Express **c** in terms of **a** and **b** and hence deduce that $T(C)$ divides $T(AB)$ in the ratio $m : n$.

7 The centroid of any triangle ABC is the point with position vector $\frac{1}{3}(\mathbf{a} + \mathbf{b} + \mathbf{c})$. The linear transformation T maps A, B, C to A′, B′, C′ respectively. If G is the centroid of triangle ABC, show that $T(G)$ is the centroid of triangle A′B′C′.

8 Some textbooks define T as a linear transformation if

(i) $T(k\mathbf{u}) = kT(\mathbf{u})$ and

(ii) $T(\mathbf{u} + \mathbf{v}) = T(\mathbf{u}) + T(\mathbf{v})$,

whatever the number k and whatever the vectors **u** and **v**. Show that this definition is equivalent to the one given on page 105.

9 (i) A transformation T maps the point P(x, y) to P′$(x′, y′)$, where $x′$ and $y′$ are given by $\begin{pmatrix} x′ \\ y′ \\ 1 \end{pmatrix} = \begin{pmatrix} 1 & 0 & 3 \\ 0 & 1 & -5 \\ 0 & 0 & 1 \end{pmatrix}\begin{pmatrix} x \\ y \\ 1 \end{pmatrix}$. Is T a linear transformation?

Justify your answer and describe the transformation as simply as possible.

(ii) Find a similar matrix method of representing a 90° anticlockwise rotation about the point (2, 1). Is this a linear transformation?

10 Quadratic functions may be represented by points in three-dimensional space as follows: the point (a, b, c) represents $ax^2 + bx + c$. In a similar way we may represent linear functions by points in two-dimensional space. Show that differentiating quadratic functions may be regarded as a linear transformation, and find the matrix which represents differentiation of fourth-degree polynomials.

Determinants of 2 × 2 matrices

On page 94 the determinant of the 2×2 matrix $\mathbf{M} = \begin{pmatrix} a & c \\ b & d \end{pmatrix}$ was defined as the number $ad - bc$. It is denoted in several ways: det **M**, |**M**|, or $\begin{vmatrix} a & c \\ b & d \end{vmatrix}$.

The following Activity shows the geometrical significance of determinants.

ACTIVITY

(i) Figure 5.16 shows the unit square and its image under **T**, defined by matrix $\mathbf{T} = \begin{pmatrix} 3 & 1 \\ 1 & 2 \end{pmatrix}$. Explain why the image is a parallelogram, find its area and evaluate det **T**.

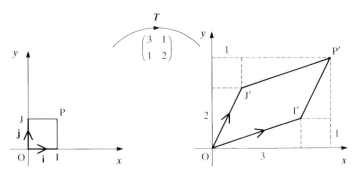

Figure 5.16

(ii) Transformations **R** and **S** are defined by the matrices $\mathbf{R} = \begin{pmatrix} 3 & 5 \\ 1 & 1 \end{pmatrix}$ and $\mathbf{S} = \begin{pmatrix} 3 & 6 \\ 1 & 2 \end{pmatrix}$. Apply **R** and **S** to the unit square. Find the areas of the images, and evaluate det **R** and det **S**.

(iii) Comment on what you notice.

Ignoring (for the moment) the sign of the determinant, you will have found that the determinant is the area scale factor for the transformation. If you move anticlockwise around the original shape (the unit square) you come to the vertices O, I, P, J, in that order; moving around the images in the same order you are again moving anticlockwise in (i), but you are moving clockwise in (ii). It is this reversal of *sense* that is indicated by the negative sign of det **R** in (ii).

ACTIVITY

Figure 5.17 shows rectangle PQRS with horizontal and vertical sides of lengths h, k respectively, together with its image P′Q′R′S′ under **T**, defined by matrix $\mathbf{T} = \begin{pmatrix} a & c \\ b & d \end{pmatrix}$. You may assume that det **T** is positive.

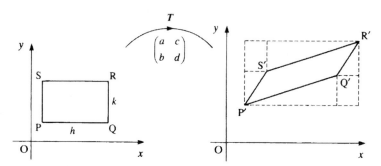

Figure 5.17

Show that $\overrightarrow{P'Q'} = \begin{pmatrix} ha \\ hb \end{pmatrix}$. Find $\overrightarrow{P'S'}$ and deduce that the area of P′Q′R′S′ is the area of PQRS × det **T**.

The area of any plane shape can be found as accurately you want as the sum of a number of sufficiently small squares. When a shape is transformed by T, with matrix $\mathbf{T} = \begin{pmatrix} a & c \\ b & d \end{pmatrix}$, the area of each of these squares is multiplied by the same scale factor, $\det \mathbf{T} = ad - bc$. Thus $ad - bc$ is the area scale factor for the transformation. Strictly you should say that $\det \mathbf{T} = ad - bc$ is the *signed* area scale factor, as it can be negative, signifying that the sense (clockwise or anticlockwise) has been reversed.

 ACTIVITY

$\mathbf{M}$ is the matrix representing reflection of the plane in the line $y = x\tan\theta$. Show that $\det \mathbf{M} = -1$ and draw a diagram to demonstrate that vertices labelled clockwise around a shape are transformed to vertices labelled anticlockwise around the image.

❷ Find several 2×2 matrices whose determinants are 0. Apply the transformations corresponding to your matrices to shapes of your own choice. What do you notice?

If $\det \mathbf{T} = 0$ the matrix $\mathbf{T}$ is said to be *singular*, and the transformation represented by $\mathbf{T} = \begin{pmatrix} a & c \\ b & d \end{pmatrix}$ maps the whole plane on to a single line P′Q′ (which passes through the origin, as shown in figure 5.18) or on to a single point (which has to be the origin, and that only happens if $\mathbf{T} = \begin{pmatrix} 0 & 0 \\ 0 & 0 \end{pmatrix}$, the zero matrix).

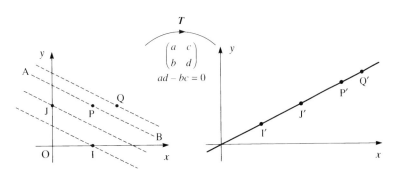

Figure 5.18

Each point in the range (i.e. each point on line P′Q′) is the image of infinitely many points in the domain. All the points which map to P′ fall on a straight line, labelled AB in figure 5.18, and every point on AB maps to P′. I′ is also the image of all points on a line through I parallel to AB. Each point on a line through Q parallel to AB maps to Q′.

Prove that the general point P(x, y) maps to P′ on the line $bx - ay = 0$ when the plane is transformed using the matrix $\begin{pmatrix} a & c \\ b & d \end{pmatrix}$, where $ad - bc = 0$.

We now prove that if det $\mathbf{M} \neq 0$, distinct points A, B will have distinct images, A′, B′ under the transformation represented by $\mathbf{M}$. To do this consider a third point C not on line AB. Then triangle ABC has non-zero area, S say. It was proved earlier that the area of the image triangle A′B′C′ is $S \times$ det $\mathbf{M}$. This is not zero as neither S nor det $\mathbf{M}$ is zero. Therefore, A′, B′, C′ are distinct points (and not on the same straight line).

1 Find the values of the determinants of the following matrices and decide whether the matrices are singular or non-singular.

(i) $\begin{pmatrix} 6 & 4 \\ 2 & 3 \end{pmatrix}$ **(ii)** $\begin{pmatrix} 4 & 8 \\ -1 & -2 \end{pmatrix}$ **(iii)** $\begin{pmatrix} 5 & 3 \\ 1 & \frac{3}{5} \end{pmatrix}$ **(iv)** $\begin{pmatrix} 1 & -2 \\ 2 & 3 \end{pmatrix}$

2 Show that the determinant of the matrix representing rotation of the plane through angle α anticlockwise about the origin is 1.

3 By considering the geometrical significance of the determinant, explain why $\det(\mathbf{MN}) = \det \mathbf{M} \times \det \mathbf{N}$, and check the result numerically using 2×2 matrices $\mathbf{M}$ and $\mathbf{N}$ of your own choice.

4 The two-way stretch with matrix $\begin{pmatrix} a & 0 \\ 0 & d \end{pmatrix}$ preserves area. What is the relationship connecting a and d?

5 The point P is projected to P′ on the line $3y = x$, so that PP′ is parallel to $y = 3x$. Find the image of the point (s, t) and hence find the matrix representing this transformation. Show that the determinant of the matrix is 0.

6 The plane is transformed by means of the matrix $\mathbf{M} = \begin{pmatrix} 2 & 4 \\ 1 & 2 \end{pmatrix}$.

(i) Show that det $\mathbf{M} = 0$, and that the whole plane is mapped on to the line $x - 2y = 0$.

(ii) The point P(x, y) is mapped to P′(4, 2). Use the equation $\mathbf{p}' = \mathbf{Mp}$ to show that P could be any point on the line $x + 2y = 2$.

(iii) Find the equation of the line of points that map to (10, 5).

7 The points P, Q and R have co-ordinates (x_p, y_p), (x_q, y_q) and (x_r, y_r) respectively. Show that the area of triangle OPQ is $\pm \frac{1}{2} \begin{vmatrix} x_p & x_q \\ y_p & y_q \end{vmatrix}$.

Hence show that the area of triangle PQR is $\pm \frac{1}{2} \begin{vmatrix} x_p - x_r & x_q - x_r \\ y_p - y_r & y_q - y_r \end{vmatrix}$.

8 Shear S moves each point parallel to the fixed line $y = x \tan\alpha$. Each point moves k times its distance from the fixed line. Show that the matrix for this transformation is $\begin{pmatrix} 1 + k\sin\alpha\cos\alpha & -k\cos^2\alpha \\ k\sin^2\alpha & 1 - k\sin\alpha\cos\alpha \end{pmatrix}$.

Hence show that shears preserve area.

9 The equations $\begin{cases} a_1x + b_1y = c_1 \\ a_2x + b_2y = c_2 \end{cases}$ may be written as $x\mathbf{a} + y\mathbf{b} = \mathbf{c}$, where $\mathbf{a} = \begin{pmatrix} a_1 \\ a_2 \end{pmatrix}$ etc.

Show that the solution is $x = \dfrac{|\mathbf{c}\ \ \mathbf{b}|}{|\mathbf{a}\ \ \mathbf{b}|}$, $y = \dfrac{|\mathbf{a}\ \ \mathbf{c}|}{|\mathbf{a}\ \ \mathbf{b}|}$ where $|\mathbf{a}\ \ \mathbf{b}|$ stands for $\begin{vmatrix} a_1 & b_1 \\ a_2 & b_2 \end{vmatrix}$,

the determinant of the matrix $\begin{pmatrix} a_1 & b_1 \\ a_2 & b_2 \end{pmatrix}$ etc.

Note particularly the positions of $\mathbf{c}$ in the determinant in the numerators of the expressions for x and y. (This is the 2×2 version of what is known as *Cramer's rule*, first published by Gabriel Cramer in 1750 though it appears to have been known by Maclaurin as early as 1729.)

Matrices and simultaneous equations

Solving the simultaneous equations $\begin{cases} x' = ax + cy \\ y' = bx + dy \end{cases}$ may be regarded as solving the

matrix equation: $\mathbf{M}\begin{pmatrix} x \\ y \end{pmatrix} = \begin{pmatrix} e \\ f \end{pmatrix}$, where $\mathbf{M} = \begin{pmatrix} a & c \\ b & d \end{pmatrix}$.

If $\det \mathbf{M} \neq 0$, $\mathbf{M}^{-1}$ exists, and pre-multiplying both sides by $\mathbf{M}^{-1}$ gives

$$\mathbf{M}^{-1}\mathbf{M}\begin{pmatrix} x \\ y \end{pmatrix} = \mathbf{M}^{-1}\begin{pmatrix} e \\ f \end{pmatrix}$$

$$\Rightarrow \quad \begin{pmatrix} x \\ y \end{pmatrix} = \mathbf{M}^{-1}\begin{pmatrix} e \\ f \end{pmatrix}.$$

EXAMPLE 5.8 Solve the equations $\begin{cases} 3x + 2y = 9 \\ 4x + 5y = 5 \end{cases}$ simultaneously.

SOLUTION

The equations may be rewritten as the single matrix equation

$$\begin{pmatrix} 3 & 2 \\ 4 & 5 \end{pmatrix}\begin{pmatrix} x \\ y \end{pmatrix} = \begin{pmatrix} 9 \\ 5 \end{pmatrix}.$$

Pre-multiply both sides by $\begin{pmatrix} 3 & 2 \\ 4 & 5 \end{pmatrix}^{-1} = \dfrac{1}{7}\begin{pmatrix} 5 & -2 \\ -4 & 3 \end{pmatrix}$ to get

$$\frac{1}{7}\begin{pmatrix} 5 & -2 \\ -4 & 3 \end{pmatrix}\begin{pmatrix} 3 & 2 \\ 4 & 5 \end{pmatrix}\begin{pmatrix} x \\ y \end{pmatrix} = \frac{1}{7}\begin{pmatrix} 5 & -2 \\ -4 & 3 \end{pmatrix}\begin{pmatrix} 9 \\ 5 \end{pmatrix}.$$

As $\mathbf{M}^{-1}\mathbf{M}\mathbf{p} = \mathbf{p}$, the left-hand side simplifies to $\begin{pmatrix} x \\ y \end{pmatrix}$, giving

$$\begin{pmatrix} x \\ y \end{pmatrix} = \frac{1}{7}\begin{pmatrix} 35 \\ -21 \end{pmatrix}.$$

The solution is $x = 5$, $y = -3$.

Solving the simultaneous equations $\begin{cases} x' = ax + cy \\ y' = bx + dy \end{cases}$ may be interpreted in two ways.

INTERPRETATION A

The two equations may be regarded as the equations of two lines in a plane. You are looking for points common to both lines. The two lines may

(i) cross, at a single common point, as shown in figure 5.19: the equations have a unique solution;

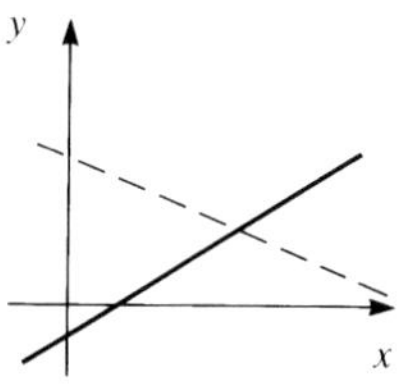

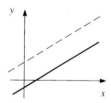

Figure 5.19

or

(ii) have no common points because they are distinct parallel lines, as shown in figure 5.20: the equations have no solution and we say that the equations are *inconsistent*;

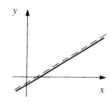

Figure 5.20

or

(iii) be coincident lines, having all their points in common, as shown in figure 5.21: the equations have infinitely many solutions, which may be expressed in terms of a single parameter.

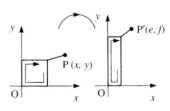

Figure 5.21

INTERPRETATION B

Here you are dealing with a transformation of the plane, with matrix **M**. The co-ordinates of P′ are given as (e, f) and you are looking for the co-ordinates of P, the point that is mapped to P′. Either det $\mathbf{M} \neq 0$, as described in **(i)** below, or det $\mathbf{M} = 0$, giving rise to situation **(ii)** or **(iii)** below.

(i) If det $\mathbf{M} \neq 0$, **M** is non-singular, $\mathbf{M}^{-1}$ exists, and there is a unique position for P, as shown in figure 5.22, and a unique solution to the equations.

Figure 5.22

If det $\mathbf{M} = 0$, $\mathbf{M}$ is singular, $\mathbf{M}^{-1}$ does not exist, and the transformation maps all points on to a single line l (through the origin); whether we have a solution or not depends on whether P′ is on l or not.

(ii) If P′ is not on l, then P′ is not the image of any point: the equations have no solution; the equations are inconsistent (figure 5.23).

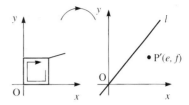

Figure 5.23

(iii) If P′ is on l, then there are infinitely many possible positions for P, all the points on a certain line (figure 5.24): the equations have infinitely many solutions, which may be expressed in terms of a single parameter.

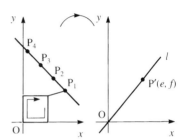

Figure 5.24

Throughout Interpretation B you have assumed that $\mathbf{M}$ is not the zero matrix, a trivial and obvious situation in which all points of the plane are mapped to the origin. There will be no solution if P′ is not at the origin. If P′ is at the origin, P may be anywhere on the plane: x and y may take any values.

Similarly the three simultaneous equations in three variables

$$a_1 x + b_1 y + c_1 z = d_1$$
$$a_2 x + b_2 y + c_2 z = d_2$$
$$a_3 x + b_3 y + c_3 z = d_3$$

are equivalent to the matrix equation $\mathbf{M}\begin{pmatrix} x \\ y \\ z \end{pmatrix} = \begin{pmatrix} d_1 \\ d_2 \\ d_3 \end{pmatrix}$, where $\mathbf{M} = \begin{pmatrix} a_1 & b_1 & c_1 \\ a_2 & b_2 & c_2 \\ a_3 & b_3 & c_3 \end{pmatrix}$.

The three equations may be regarded as the equations of three planes in three-dimensional space. There are seven possible configurations.

(i) If det $\mathbf{M} \neq 0$, $\mathbf{M}$ is non-singular, $\mathbf{M}^{-1}$ exists, and the equations have a unique solution. This corresponds to the three planes having a single common point, figure 5.25.

Figure 5.25

If det $\mathbf{M} = 0$, $\mathbf{M}$ is singular and $\mathbf{M}^{-1}$ does not exist: in this case either the equations are inconsistent and have no solutions, see **(ii)** below; or the equations have infinitely many solutions, see **(iii)** below.

(ii) The equations being inconsistent and having no solutions corresponds to the three planes having no common point. When this happens

(a) the three planes form a triangular prism, figure 5.26;

or

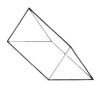

Figure 5.26

(b) two planes are parallel and distinct, and crossed by the third plane, figure 5.27;

or

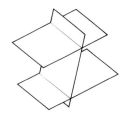

Figure 5.27

(c) two planes are coincident and the third plane is parallel but distinct, figure 5.28;

or

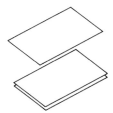

Figure 5.28

(d) all three planes are parallel and distinct, figure 5.29.

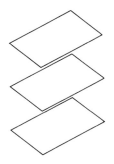

Figure 5.29

(iii) The equations having infinitely many solutions corresponds to the three planes having infinitely many common points. When this happens

either

(a) the three planes have a line of common points: this arrangement is known as a *sheaf* or *pencil* of planes, figure 5.30; the solutions are given in terms of a single parameter;

Figure 5.30

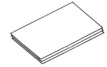

or

(b) the three planes all coincide, figure 5.31: the solutions are given in terms of two parameters.

Figure 5.31

Again we have ignored the trivial situation where **M** consists entirely of zeros. Figure 5.32 summarises the decisions that need to be made.

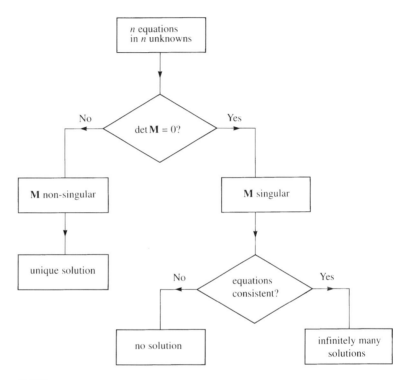

Figure 5.32

EXAMPLE 5.9

Investigate the solution of the equations $\begin{cases} x + 3y - 2z = 7 & \text{A} \\ 2x - 2y + z = 3 & \text{B} \\ 3x + y - z = k & \text{C} \end{cases}$

(i) when $k = 10$;

(ii) when $k = 12$.

SOLUTION

Start by eliminating one variable (z) to obtain two equations in x, y.

$$\text{A} - 2\text{C}: \quad -5x + y = 7 - 2k \quad \Rightarrow \quad 5x - y = -7 + 2k$$
$$\text{B} + \text{C}: \quad 5x - y = 3 + k.$$

Now $5x - y$ can only equal $-7 + 2k$ and $3 + k$ if

$$-7 + 2k = 3 + k$$
$$\Leftrightarrow \quad k = 10.$$

(i) When $k = 10$, equations A – 2C and B + C both reduce to $5x - y = 13$, so you can only solve for x and y (and later z) in terms of a parameter. If $x = \lambda$, $y = 5\lambda - 13$ and from equation C you get:

$$z = 3\lambda + 5\lambda - 13 - 10 = 8\lambda - 23.$$

You have a line of solution points, which can be given in terms of a single parameter: $(\lambda, 5\lambda - 13, 8\lambda - 23)$. The three planes are arranged as a sheaf.

(ii) When $k = 12$, equations A – 2C and B + C are inconsistent as $5x - y$ cannot be both 17 and 15.

Equations A and B are the same as in **(i)**, so the corresponding planes have not changed. In equation C the value of k has changed from 10 to 12, causing a translation of the plane.

The original equations are inconsistent. The corresponding planes form a triangular prism.

ALTERNATIVE APPROACHES

You are shown how to evaluate a 3×3 determinant in the Appendix on page 153. However, a calculator tells you that $\begin{vmatrix} 1 & 3 & -2 \\ 2 & -2 & 1 \\ 3 & 1 & -1 \end{vmatrix} = 0$, so you know that you do not have a unique solution, but either no solutions or many solutions.

The normals corresponding to the equations A, B, C are clearly not parallel, so your three planes are not parallel (or identical): you can only be dealing with a sheaf of planes or a triangular prism.

Examination of the equations shows that C = A + B when $k = 10$, so that the equations are not inconsistent in **(i)** and you then have a sheaf of planes, their common line being the line of solution points. (If you want to find expressions for these points you can use algebraic methods, as in the first solution, or use vector methods, as explained in Chapter 3, page 47.)

As before, changing the value of k translates the plane represented by C, but does not affect the other two planes so in **(ii)** the three planes form a triangular prism and the equations are inconsistent.

EXERCISE 5F

In Questions 1–10 decide whether the equations are consistent or inconsistent. If they are consistent, solve them, in terms of a parameter if necessary. In each question also describe the configuration of the corresponding lines or planes.

1 $3x + 5y = 17$
$2x + 4y = 11$

2 $3x + 6y = 12$
$2x + 4y = 15$

3 $6x - 3y = 12$
$2x - y = 4$

4 $8x - 4y = 11$
$y = 2x - 4$

5 $x + y + z = 4$
$2x + 3y - 4z = 3$
$5x + 8y - 13z = 8$

6 $2x - y = 1$
$3x + 2z = 13$
$3y + 4z = 23$

7 $x + 2y + 4z = 7$
$3x + 2y + 5z = 21$
$4x + y + 2z = 14$

8 $3x + 2y + z = 2$
$5x + 3y - 4z = 1$
$x + y + 4z = 5$

9 $2x + y - z = 5$
$8x + 4y - 4z = 20$
$-2x - y + z = -5$

10 $5x + 3y - 2z = 6$
$6x + 2y + 3z = 11$
$7x + y + 8z = 12$

11 Find the two values of k for which the equations $\begin{cases} 2x - ky = 3 \\ kx + 8y = 6 \end{cases}$ do not have a unique solution. In both cases find the solution set for the equations.

12 Given that det $\mathbf{M} = 0$, where $\mathbf{M}$ is a 2×2 matrix, explain why $\mathbf{M}\begin{pmatrix} x \\ y \end{pmatrix} = \begin{pmatrix} p \\ q \end{pmatrix}$ has infinitely many solutions if both p and q are zero.

What happens if p and q are not both zero?

13 Solve the equation $\begin{pmatrix} 1 & 3 & -2 \\ -3 & 1 & 1 \\ -3 & 11 & -4 \end{pmatrix}\begin{pmatrix} x \\ y \\ z \end{pmatrix} = \begin{pmatrix} -2 \\ 6 \\ k \end{pmatrix}$ in each of the two cases

(i) $k = 3$

(ii) $k = 6$,

giving x, y and z in terms of a parameter λ if appropriate. In both cases interpret your solution geometrically with reference to three appropriate planes.

14 You are given the matrices

$$\mathbf{P} = \begin{pmatrix} -2 & 26 & -16 \\ 1 & -11 & 7 \\ -1 & 21 & -13 \end{pmatrix} \text{ and } \mathbf{Q} = \begin{pmatrix} -2 & 1 & k \\ 3 & 5 & -1 \\ 5 & 8 & -2 \end{pmatrix}.$$

(i)   Calculate the matrix product $\mathbf{PQ}$.

(ii) For the case $k = 3$, write down the inverse matrix $\mathbf{Q}^{-1}$ and hence solve the equation

$$\mathbf{Q}\begin{pmatrix} x \\ y \\ z \end{pmatrix} = \begin{pmatrix} 19 \\ 4 \\ 5 \end{pmatrix}.$$

(iii) For the case $k = 5$, you are given that $\mathbf{Q}$ has no inverse. Solve the equation

$$\mathbf{Q}\begin{pmatrix} x \\ y \\ z \end{pmatrix} = \begin{pmatrix} 19 \\ 4 \\ 5 \end{pmatrix},$$

giving x, y and z in terms of a parameter t.

(iv) Describe how the three planes

$-2x + y + 5z = 19$
$3x + 5y - z = 4$
$5x + 8y - 2z = 5$

intersect.

15 **A** is a 3×3 matrix and **d** is a 3×1 column vector. Show that all solutions of the equation $\mathbf{Ar} = \mathbf{d}$ can be expressed in the form $\mathbf{r} = \mathbf{p} + \mathbf{k}$, where **p** is any particular solution (of $\mathbf{Ar} = \mathbf{d}$) and **k** is any solution of the related equation $\mathbf{Ar} = \mathbf{0}$. Does it matter if **A** is singular or non-singular?

(If you are studying *Mechanics 4* you should compare what you have just done with the solution of linear differential equations by the method of particular integral and complementary function.)

16 Show that the equations $\begin{cases} 3x + 2y = 4 \\ 2x - 3y = 7 \\ 5x - 4y = k \end{cases}$ are inconsistent unless k takes one

particular value, which you should state.

17 You are given the matrix

$$\mathbf{M} = \begin{pmatrix} 3 & 1 & -3 \\ 4 & -2 & 1 \\ 5 & -3 & 2 \end{pmatrix}.$$

(i) Show that $\det \mathbf{M} = 0$.

(ii) Solve the equation

$$\mathbf{M} \begin{pmatrix} x \\ y \\ z \end{pmatrix} = \begin{pmatrix} 2 \\ 6 \\ k \end{pmatrix}$$

in each of the two cases

(a) $k = 3$

(b) $k = 8$,

giving x, y and z in terms of a parameter t if appropriate.

In each case interpret your solution geometrically with reference to the three planes

$$3x + y - 3z = 2$$
$$4x - 2y + z = 6$$
$$5x - 3y + 2z = k.$$

[MEI]

Invariance

Invariant points

In any rotation, the centre C of the rotation maps to itself (figure 5.33). C is an example of an *invariant point*. In a reflection, points on the mirror line do not move – a further example of invariant points.

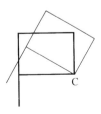

Figure 5.33

The product $\begin{pmatrix} 6 & 5 \\ 2 & 3 \end{pmatrix}\begin{pmatrix} 2 \\ -2 \end{pmatrix} = \begin{pmatrix} 2 \\ -2 \end{pmatrix}$. This means that the transformation with matrix $\begin{pmatrix} 6 & 5 \\ 2 & 3 \end{pmatrix}$ maps the point $(2, -2)$ to itself. This is another example of an invariant point.

ACTIVITY

Explain why the origin is always an invariant point in a linear transformation.

EXAMPLE 5.10

Find the invariant points under the transformation given by the matrix $\begin{pmatrix} 2 & -1 \\ 1 & 0 \end{pmatrix}$.

SOLUTION

Suppose $\begin{pmatrix} x \\ y \end{pmatrix}$ maps to itself. Then

$$\begin{pmatrix} 2 & -1 \\ 1 & 0 \end{pmatrix}\begin{pmatrix} x \\ y \end{pmatrix} = \begin{pmatrix} x \\ y \end{pmatrix}$$

$$\Leftrightarrow \begin{pmatrix} 2x - y \\ x \end{pmatrix} = \begin{pmatrix} x \\ y \end{pmatrix}$$

$$\Leftrightarrow 2x - y = x \text{ and } x = y$$

$$\Leftrightarrow x = y.$$

Thus all points on the line $y = x$ (and only points on this line) map on to themselves. This is a line of invariant points. (It is also an example of an invariant line.)

Invariant lines

The line AB is known as an *invariant line* under **T** if the image of each point on AB is on AB. It is important to note that it is not necessary for points on AB to map on to themselves (as in Example 5.10), but merely that each point on AB maps to a point on AB.

Occasionally it is easy to spot which lines are invariant: for example, in a reflection, as well as the mirror line being invariant (because it is a line of invariant points), each line perpendicular to the mirror line is invariant, as illustrated in figure 5.34. Because the mirror line is a line of invariant points it is sometimes described as 'pointwise invariant'.

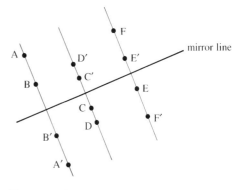

Figure 5.34

The following examples illustrate the usual methods of identifying invariant lines.

EXAMPLE 5.11

A transformation is defined by the matrix $\begin{pmatrix} 3 & 2 \\ 1 & 2 \end{pmatrix}$. Find the invariant lines which pass through the origin, and illustrate the transformation diagramatically.

SOLUTION

Consider a general point on the line $y = mx$, such as $\begin{pmatrix} X \\ mX \end{pmatrix}$.

This maps to $\begin{pmatrix} 3 & 2 \\ 1 & 2 \end{pmatrix}\begin{pmatrix} X \\ mX \end{pmatrix} = \begin{pmatrix} 3X + 2mX \\ X + 2mX \end{pmatrix}$ and you want this image to be a point on the same line, $y = mx$, so

$$X + 2mX = m(3X + 2mX)$$
$$\Leftrightarrow \quad X(2m^2 + m - 1) = 0.$$

You want this to hold for all values of X, including non-zero values, so

$$2m^2 + m - 1 = 0$$
$$\Leftrightarrow \quad (2m - 1)(m + 1) = 0$$
$$\Leftrightarrow \quad m = \tfrac{1}{2} \ \text{ or } \ m = -1.$$

Using these values of m, the invariant lines are $y = \tfrac{1}{2}x$ and $x + y = 0$.

But $y = mx$ and $\begin{pmatrix} X \\ mX \end{pmatrix}$ do not cover all possible lines through the origin:

you also need to consider the vertical line $x = 0$. The general point on this line is $(0, Y)$. The image of this point is $(2Y, 2Y)$, which is not on the line $x = 0$ (unless $Y = 0$), so you can conclude that the vertical line through the origin is not invariant under this transformation.

The transformation is illustrated in figure 5.35, where the dashed lines are the invariant lines $y = \tfrac{1}{2}x$ and $x + y = 0$, with the latter being pointwise invariant, a line of invariant points.

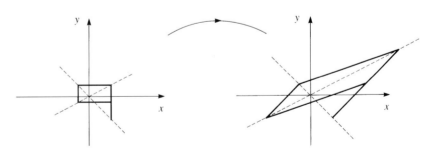

Figure 5.35

EXAMPLE 5.12

A transformation is defined by the matrix $\begin{pmatrix} 2 & -1 \\ 1 & 0 \end{pmatrix}$. Find the invariant lines.

SOLUTION

Consider a general point on the line $y = mx + c$, such as $\begin{pmatrix} X \\ mX + c \end{pmatrix}$.

This maps to $\begin{pmatrix} 2 & -1 \\ 1 & 0 \end{pmatrix}\begin{pmatrix} X \\ mX + c \end{pmatrix} = \begin{pmatrix} 2X - mX - c \\ X \end{pmatrix}$ and you want this image to be a point on the same line, $y = mx + c$, so

$$X = m(2X - mX - c) + c$$
$$\Leftrightarrow \quad X(m^2 - 2m + 1) = c(1 - m). \qquad \qquad \text{①}$$

This is to hold for all values of X.

Putting $X = 0$ gives $c(1 - m) = 0$.

This, plus putting $X \neq 0$, gives $m^2 - 2m + 1 = 0$.

Therefore

$$m^2 - 2m + 1 = c(1 - m) = 0$$
$$\Leftrightarrow \quad (1 - m)^2 = c(1 - m) = 0 \qquad \qquad \text{②}$$

so that $m = 1$.

From ②: when $m = 1$, c can take any value.

All lines with gradient 1 are invariant, but the line $y = x$ is a line of invariant points. Figure 5.36 shows what is happening.

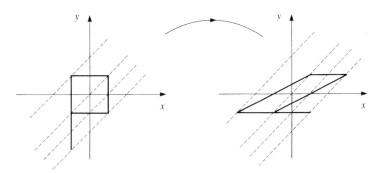

Figure 5.36

The analysis above deals with all lines except vertical ones. It is clear from the diagram that no vertical line remains invariant, or it may be proved algebraically as in Example 5.11.

The transformation is a shear parallel to $y = x$ and all lines parallel to $y = x$ are invariant.

A first glance at equation ① in Example 5.12 suggests you are attempting to solve a single equation in three unknowns. But you want this relationship to hold for all values of X: in effect you can construct equations in m and c by choosing values of X.

EXAMPLE 5.13   Find the invariant lines of the transformation with matrix $\begin{pmatrix} 0.2 & 0.4 \\ 0.4 & 0.8 \end{pmatrix}$.

SOLUTION

In this example the matrix is singular, and all points map on to a straight line. Consider a general point on the line $y = mx + c$, such as $\begin{pmatrix} X \\ mX + c \end{pmatrix}$.

This maps to

$$\begin{pmatrix} 0.2 & 0.4 \\ 0.4 & 0.8 \end{pmatrix} \begin{pmatrix} X \\ mX + c \end{pmatrix} = \begin{pmatrix} 0.2X + 0.4mX + 0.4c \\ 0.4X + 0.8mX + 0.8c \end{pmatrix}$$

and you want this image to be a point on the same line, $y = mx + c$, so

$$0.4X + 0.8mX + 0.8c = m(0.2X + 0.4mX + 0.4c) + c$$
$$\Leftrightarrow 0.2X(2m^2 - 3m - 2) = -0.2c(1 + 2m).$$

This is to hold for all values of X, so, as in Example 5.12,

$$2m^2 - 3m - 2 = -0.2c(1 + 2m) = 0$$
$$\Leftrightarrow (2m + 1)(m - 2) = -0.2c(1 + 2m) = 0 \qquad \textcircled{1}$$

so that $m = 2$ or $-\frac{1}{2}$.

From $\textcircled{1}$: $m = 2 \Rightarrow c = 0$, but when $m = -\frac{1}{2}$, c may take any value. Again a diagram is informative (see figure 5.37).

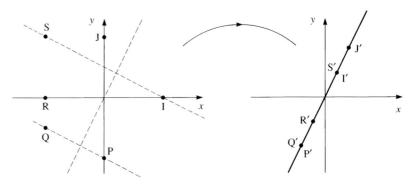

Figure 5.37

The line $y = 2x$ is invariant: it is the line to which all points are mapped in this transformation, and is in fact a line of invariant points.

The line $y = -\frac{1}{2}x + \frac{1}{2}$, passes through the point I; all points on this line map to I′ (0.2, 0.4), which is itself a point on $y = -\frac{1}{2}x + \frac{1}{2}$, so the line $y = -\frac{1}{2}x + \frac{1}{2}$ is regarded as an example of an invariant line – a 'degenerate' example.

For this transformation a similar discussion applies to all lines parallel to $y = -\frac{1}{2}x + \frac{1}{2}$.

This transformation projects all points perpendicularly on to the line $y = 2x$. It is known as an *orthogonal projection*.

You need to check what happens to vertical lines. One approach is to use your understanding of what this projection does; alternatively, the general point (c, Y) on the vertical line $x = c$ maps to $(0.2c + 0.4Y, 0.4c + 0.8Y)$ which, given c, is not on $x = c$ for all values of Y. No vertical lines are invariant under this transformation.

The invariant lines are $y = 2x$ and (degenerately) all lines of the form $y = -\frac{1}{2}x + c$.

As illustrated in Example 5.13, it is important to note that AB is defined as invariant if each point on AB transforms to a point on AB. It is not necessary for every point on AB to be the image of a point on AB. However, these degenerate invariant lines can only occur if the determinant of the defining matrix is zero.

ACTIVITY

On page 105 you saw that under a linear transformation, the image of a line is a line. The proof concluded with the sentence:

Thus $\mathbf{r'} = \mathbf{a'} + \lambda \mathbf{d'}$, which is the equation of a straight line, provided (for the moment) that $\mathbf{d'} \neq \mathbf{0}$.

Comment on the restriction on $\mathbf{d'}$.

EXERCISE 5G

In Questions 1–4, find the invariant points for the transformations with the given matrices.

1 $\begin{pmatrix} 0 & -1 \\ 1 & 2 \end{pmatrix}$ **2** $\begin{pmatrix} 3 & 4 \\ 1 & 2 \end{pmatrix}$ **3** $\begin{pmatrix} 0.6 & 0.8 \\ 0.8 & -0.6 \end{pmatrix}$ **4** $\begin{pmatrix} \frac{1}{\sqrt{2}} & -\frac{1}{\sqrt{2}} \\ -\frac{1}{\sqrt{2}} & \frac{1}{\sqrt{2}} \end{pmatrix}$

In Questions 5–8 for the transformations with the given matrices find the invariant lines which pass through the origin.

5 $\begin{pmatrix} -3 & 4 \\ 4 & 3 \end{pmatrix}$ **6** $\begin{pmatrix} 1 & 0 \\ 2 & 2 \end{pmatrix}$ **7** $\begin{pmatrix} 1.36 & 0.48 \\ 0.48 & 1.64 \end{pmatrix}$ **8** $\begin{pmatrix} \frac{1}{2} & \frac{1}{4} \\ 1 & \frac{1}{2} \end{pmatrix}$

In Questions 9–12, find all the invariant lines for the transformations with the given matrices.

9 $\begin{pmatrix} -1 & 2 \\ -2 & 3 \end{pmatrix}$ **10** $\begin{pmatrix} 10 & 3 \\ 3 & 2 \end{pmatrix}$ **11** $\begin{pmatrix} 2 & -1 \\ -1 & 2 \end{pmatrix}$ **12** $\begin{pmatrix} 3\frac{1}{2} & -\frac{1}{2} \\ -\frac{1}{2} & 3\frac{1}{2} \end{pmatrix}$

13 The matrix $\mathbf{M} = \begin{pmatrix} 4 & 3 \\ 9 & 10 \end{pmatrix}$ transforms the point (x, y) to (x', y'), where

$$\begin{pmatrix} x' \\ y' \end{pmatrix} = \begin{pmatrix} 4 & 3 \\ 9 & 10 \end{pmatrix} \begin{pmatrix} x \\ y \end{pmatrix}.$$

(i) By considering the image of $(1, m)$ under the transformation given by $\mathbf{M}$, or otherwise, find the two values of m for which $y = mx$ is an invariant line of the transformation.

(ii) Draw a sketch showing these two invariant lines, and for both values of m indicate how the point $(1, m)$ is transformed by **M**.

(iii) Show that $y = 3x + 4$ is also an invariant line under this transformation.

[MEI]

14 The transformation T maps $\begin{pmatrix} x \\ y \end{pmatrix}$ to $\begin{pmatrix} a & c \\ b & d \end{pmatrix}\begin{pmatrix} x \\ y \end{pmatrix}$, where a, b, c, d are not all zero.

Show that all lines through the origin are invariant under T if and only if $b = c = 0$ and $a = d \neq 0$.

15 The point P(x, y) is mapped on to the point P$'(x', y')$ by the transformation

$$\begin{pmatrix} x' \\ y' \end{pmatrix} = \mathbf{A}\begin{pmatrix} x \\ y \end{pmatrix} \text{ where } \mathbf{A} = \begin{pmatrix} 1 & -1 \\ 3 & -3 \end{pmatrix}.$$

(i) What is the value of the determinant of the matrix **A**?

(ii) The point Q$(1, m)$ is transformed into the point Q$'(k, km)$. Find the values of k and m. Hence give the equations of the invariant lines of the transformation.

(iii) Draw a sketch and describe the transformation of the plane represented by **A** with reference to the points on the lines $y = x$, $y = x + 1$, $y = x - 2$.

(iv) Which points transform to the point $(3, 9)$?

[MEI]

16 The matrix $\mathbf{M} = \begin{pmatrix} 3 & 6 \\ -1 & -4 \end{pmatrix}$ transforms the point (x, y) to (x', y'), where

$$\begin{pmatrix} x' \\ y' \end{pmatrix} = \begin{pmatrix} 3 & 6 \\ -1 & -4 \end{pmatrix}\begin{pmatrix} x \\ y \end{pmatrix}.$$

(i) Show that the origin $(0, 0)$ is the only invariant point under this transformation.

(ii) By considering the image of $(1, m)$ under the transformation given by **M**, or otherwise, find the two values of m for which $y = mx$ is an invariant line of the transformation.

(iii) The line L is transformed by **M** on to the line L', and L' is transformed by **M** on to the line with equation $y = 24 - 2x$. Find the equation of L.

[MEI]

17 (i) M is a reflection of the plane such that the point (x', y') is the image of the point (x, y) where

$$\begin{pmatrix} x' \\ y' \end{pmatrix} = \begin{pmatrix} -0.6 & 0.8 \\ 0.8 & 0.6 \end{pmatrix}\begin{pmatrix} x \\ y \end{pmatrix}.$$

Find a point, other than the origin, that is invariant under this reflection. Hence find the equation of the mirror line.

(ii) T is a translation of the plane by the vector $\begin{pmatrix} a \\ b \end{pmatrix}$. The point (X, Y) is the image of the point (x, y) under the combined transformation TM (that is M followed by T), where

$$\begin{pmatrix} X \\ Y \\ 1 \end{pmatrix} = \begin{pmatrix} -0.6 & 0.8 & a \\ 0.8 & 0.6 & b \\ 0 & 0 & 1 \end{pmatrix} \begin{pmatrix} x \\ y \\ 1 \end{pmatrix}.$$

(a) Show that if $a = -4$ and $b = 2$ then $(0, 5)$ is an invariant point of $\boldsymbol{TM}$.

(b) Show that if $a = 2$ and $b = 1$ then $\boldsymbol{TM}$ has no invariant point.

(c) Find a relation between a and b that must be satisfied if $\boldsymbol{TM}$ is to have any invariant points.

[SMP]

INVESTIGATIONS

1 Investigate the sequence of matrices **I, M, M**^{2}, **M**^{3}, ... where $\mathbf{M} = \begin{pmatrix} 1 & 1 \\ 1 & 0 \end{pmatrix}$.

2 Mendel's genetic theory states that offspring inherit characteristics from their parents through their genes. Each characteristic is controlled by a pair of genes, which may be of two types: G or g. The three possible combinations are

GG	known as homozygous dominant, and denoted by D
Gg or gG	known as heterozygous, and denoted by H
gg	known as homozygous recessive, and denoted by R.

Offspring inherit one gene from each parent, randomly and independently. In a controlled study of a population of fruit flies, the only females allowed to mate are those known to be heterozygous.

(i) The unfinished table shows the probability that the offspring has combination D, H or R given the combination of genes of the male parent. Complete the table to construct the matrix **M** containing this information.

Male parent

		D	H	R
Offspring	D	$\frac{1}{2}$	$\frac{1}{4}$	0
	H	...	...	...
	R	...	...	...

(ii) Initially the proportions of D, H and R combinations in the population are given by

$\mathbf{x}_0 = \begin{pmatrix} d \\ h \\ r \end{pmatrix}$. Show that $\mathbf{x}_1 = \mathbf{M}\mathbf{x}_0$ gives the proportions in the next generation.

(iii) Investigate what happens if the study continues over many generations.

3 The transformation $\boldsymbol{S}$ is represented by the matrix $\begin{pmatrix} 2 & -3 \\ 3 & 2 \end{pmatrix}$; transformation $\boldsymbol{T}$ maps the point Z on an Argand diagram (representing the complex number z) to the point which represents $z(2 + 3\mathrm{j})$. Compare the effects of $\boldsymbol{S}$ and $\boldsymbol{T}$, and investigate further.

5

Matrices

1 The matrix $\mathbf{M} = \begin{pmatrix} a & c \\ b & d \end{pmatrix}$ represents the transformation which maps the point with position vector $\begin{pmatrix} x \\ y \end{pmatrix}$ to the point with position vector $\begin{pmatrix} x' \\ y' \end{pmatrix}$, where $\begin{cases} x' = ax + cy \\ y' = bx + dy \end{cases}$.

2 The image of $\begin{pmatrix} 1 \\ 0 \end{pmatrix}$ is the first column of $\mathbf{M}$; the image of $\begin{pmatrix} 0 \\ 1 \end{pmatrix}$ is the second column of $\mathbf{M}$.

3 Matrix multiplication

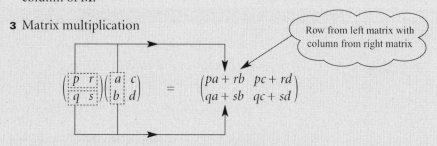

Row from left matrix with column from right matrix

$$\begin{pmatrix} p & r \\ q & s \end{pmatrix} \begin{pmatrix} a & c \\ b & d \end{pmatrix} = \begin{pmatrix} pa + rb & pc + rd \\ qa + sb & qc + sd \end{pmatrix}$$

4 Matrix multiplication is associative: $\mathbf{N(ML)} = \mathbf{(NM)L}$.

5 The *determinant* of the matrix $\mathbf{M} = \begin{pmatrix} a & c \\ b & d \end{pmatrix}$ is $ad - bc$. It is denoted by $|\mathbf{M}|$, det $\mathbf{M}$, or $\begin{vmatrix} a & c \\ b & d \end{vmatrix}$.

6 The inverse of $\mathbf{M} = \begin{pmatrix} a & c \\ b & d \end{pmatrix}$ is $\mathbf{M}^{-1} = \dfrac{1}{ad - bc} \begin{pmatrix} d & -c \\ -b & a \end{pmatrix}$, provided $ad - bc \neq 0$.

7 Note the order for the inverse of a product: $(\mathbf{AB})^{-1} = \mathbf{B}^{-1}\mathbf{A}^{-1}$.

8 If transformation T is such that $T(\lambda\mathbf{p} + \mu\mathbf{q}) = \lambda T(\mathbf{p}) + \mu T(\mathbf{q})$, whatever the scalars λ and μ, and whatever the vectors $\mathbf{p}$ and $\mathbf{q}$, then T is known as a *linear transformation*.

9 When solving n simultaneous equations in n unknowns: there is a unique solution if det $\mathbf{M} \neq 0$; if det $\mathbf{M} = 0$ there is either no solution or infinitely many solutions.

10 The line AB is known as an *invariant line* under T if the image of each point on AB is on AB.

Graphs and inequalities

Every picture is worth a thousand words.

Traditional Chinese proverb

Our culture is a visual one: we increasingly expect pictures or diagrams to illustrate ideas. Good diagrams not only help writers to communicate efficiently, but they also help students and researchers to discover and understand relationships.

You have been introduced to sketching graphs in *Pure Mathematics* 1 and 2. You will know that a sketch graph should show the essential features of the graph, such as where it cuts the axes, the nature and position of turning points, any symmetry, and the behaviour of the graph as x or y tends to infinity. You will often be satisfied with approximate location rather than exact positions. This chapter uses calculus as little as possible.

Whether you have a graphic calculator or not, aim to be able to produce your own sketch graphs without being dependent on the calculator. To be able to sketch the graph of a function accurately without using a machine demonstrates a good appreciation of the behaviour of that function. Learning to draw such sketches will help you realise how various functions behave, and why they behave like that. If you have ready access to a graphic calculator (or graph-drawing software) use it to check your sketches.

The most basic technique for drawing the graph of a function f(x) is 'dot-to-dot': choose values of x and calculate each corresponding value of f(x), usually called y, and plot these (x, y) values as points, joining them up in order of increasing x. Accuracy is improved by plotting more points, concentrating particularly on the regions where you are least certain, perhaps where the curve bends most.

Graphic calculators and graph-drawing computer programs draw graphs rapidly, many using 'dot-to-dot' methods. Sometimes the operator has the opportunity to adjust the *resolution* (or step between successive dots): smaller steps produce more accurate graphs. Even when using small steps the display should be interpreted carefully as some programs wrongly connect together separate branches of a curve.

ACTIVITY

If you have access to a graphic calculator or graph-drawing program on a computer use it to draw the graph of $y = \frac{1}{x}$ from $x = -4$ to $x = 4$ and compare the display with the diagram in figure 6.1. Try changing the x range, or the resolution.

The incorrect diagram was the output from a computer graph-drawing package.

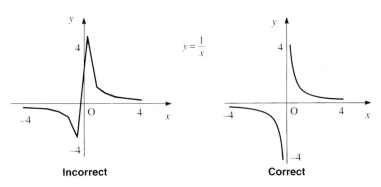

Incorrect   **Correct**

Figure 6.1

❓ **(i)**   Why is it wrong to join the two branches of $y = \frac{1}{x}$?

(ii) Is it better to join dots with straight lines or with curves?

(iii) Why do graphic calculators not display smooth curves?

Even if your graphic calculator does produce less than perfect graphs, do not throw it away! Ability to control and correctly interpret its display turns it into a valuable tool. Adjusting the *range* of the display – effectively adjusting the width and height of the window through which the graph is viewed – changes the horizontal and vertical scales. Most calculators allow you to zoom in or out. Some allow you to scroll horizontally or vertically. Unfortunately the controls are not yet standardised across the various makes of calculator, so it is inappropriate to describe them in detail here. But do experiment with them, so that you learn to use them to advantage, paying particular attention to the range controls.

Graphs of rational functions

A rational number is defined as a number which can be expressed as $\frac{n}{d}$ where the numerator n and denominator d are integers, and $d \neq 0$. In a similar way a *rational function* is defined as a function which can be expressed in the form $\frac{\text{N}(x)}{\text{D}(x)}$, where the numerator, $\text{N}(x)$, and denominator, $\text{D}(x)$, are polynomials, and $\text{D}(x)$ is not the zero polynomial. This section concentrates on how to sketch graphs of rational functions.

Consider the graph of $y = \frac{1}{x}$. If you translate it three units to the right and two units up you obtain the graph of $y = \frac{1}{x-3} + 2$ which can be rearranged as $y = \frac{2x-5}{x-3}$ (see figure 6.2.)

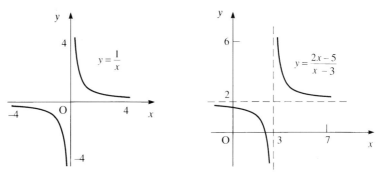

Figure 6.2

Now consider yourself moving along the curve $y = \dfrac{2x-5}{x-3}$. As your x co-ordinate gets close to 3, your y co-ordinate tends to $\pm\infty$, and you get closer and closer to the vertical line $x = 3$, shown dashed. If you move along the curve again, letting your x co-ordinate increase without limit (or decrease without limit) you get closer and closer to the horizontal line $y = 2$, also shown dashed. These dashed lines are examples of asymptotes. An *asymptote* is a straight line which a curve approaches tangentially as x and/or y tend to infinity. The line $x = 3$ is a vertical asymptote; the line $y = 2$ is a horizontal asymptote. It is usual for asymptotes to be shown by dashed lines.

In general, the line $x = a$ is a vertical asymptote for the curve $y = \dfrac{N(x)}{D(x)}$ if $D(a) = 0$ and $N(a) \neq 0$. The signs of the numerator $N(x)$ and the denominator $D(x)$ when x is close to a enable us to determine whether y tends to positive or negative infinity as x tends to a from left or from right. This is shown in sub-section **(B)** below.

Sketching the graph of $y = \dfrac{x + 2}{(x - 2)(x + 1)}$

Shown below are the steps used in building up the sketch graph.

(A) FIND WHERE THE GRAPH CUTS THE AXES

The *y intercept* is where the graph cuts the y axis. You find it by evaluating y when $x = 0$: in the case of the equation $y = \dfrac{x + 2}{(x - 2)(x + 1)}$ the y intercept is $(0, -1)$.

The *x intercept* is where the graph cuts the x axis. To find it, you put $y = 0$, and solve the resulting equation, getting, in this case, just one root, $x = -2$. You now know that this graph passes through $(0, -1)$ and $(-2, 0)$ and does not cut the axes anywhere else.

(B) EXAMINE THE BEHAVIOUR OF THE GRAPH NEAR THE VERTICAL ASYMPTOTES

The denominator of $\dfrac{x+2}{(x-2)(x+1)}$ is zero when $x=-1$ or 2, but these values do not make the numerator zero, so the vertical asymptotes are the lines $x=-1$ and $x=2$. To examine the behaviour near $x=-1$, we look at the three terms $(x+2)$, $(x-2)$ and $(x+1)$, paying particular attention to their signs (figure 6.3).

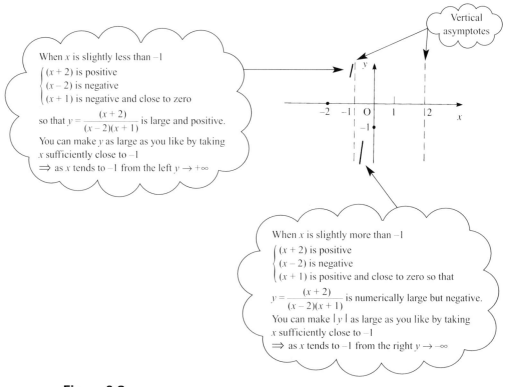

When x is slightly less than -1
$\begin{cases} (x+2) \text{ is positive} \\ (x-2) \text{ is negative} \\ (x+1) \text{ is negative and close to zero} \end{cases}$
so that $y = \dfrac{(x+2)}{(x-2)(x+1)}$ is large and positive.
You can make y as large as you like by taking x sufficiently close to -1
$\Rightarrow$ as x tends to -1 from the left $y \to +\infty$

Vertical asymptotes

When x is slightly more than -1
$\begin{cases} (x+2) \text{ is positive} \\ (x-2) \text{ is negative} \\ (x+1) \text{ is positive and close to zero so that} \end{cases}$
$y = \dfrac{(x+2)}{(x-2)(x+1)}$ is numerically large but negative.
You can make $|y|$ as large as you like by taking x sufficiently close to -1
$\Rightarrow$ as x tends to -1 from the right $y \to -\infty$

Figure 6.3

You can use a similar method to examine the behaviour of the graph as it approaches its other vertical asymptote, $x=2$. You will find that $y \to -\infty$ as $x \to 2$ from the left and $y \to +\infty$ as $x \to 2$ from the right. Figure 6.4 shows the details obtained so far.

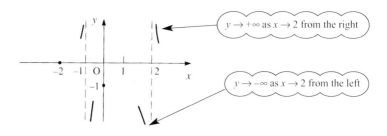

$y \to +\infty$ as $x \to 2$ from the right

$y \to -\infty$ as $x \to 2$ from the left

Figure 6.4

(C) EXAMINE THE BEHAVIOUR AS *x* TENDS TO INFINITY

Now

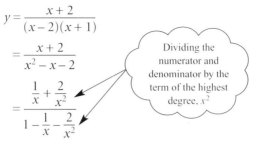

$$y = \frac{x+2}{(x-2)(x+1)}$$

$$= \frac{x+2}{x^2-x-2}$$

$$= \frac{\frac{1}{x}+\frac{2}{x^2}}{1-\frac{1}{x}-\frac{2}{x^2}}$$

Dividing the numerator and denominator by the term of the highest degree, x^2

which tends to 0 as $x \to \infty$ because $\frac{1}{x}$ and $\frac{2}{x^2} \to 0$ as $x \to \infty$.

Further, as $(x+2)$, $(x-2)$ and $(x+1)$ are all positive for large, positive x, $y \to 0$ from above as $x \to +\infty$. Similarly $y \to 0$ from below as $x \to -\infty$. The line $y = 0$ is a horizontal asymptote (figure 6.5)

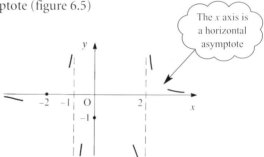

The x axis is a horizontal asymptote

Figure 6.5

(D) COMPLETE THE SKETCH

The sketch is completed in figure 6.6. Notice that this leads us to conclude that there is a local maximum between $x = -1$ and $x = 2$, and a local minimum to the left of $x = -2$. You do not know the y co-ordinate of either the minimum or the maximum. Nor have you shown that there are no other turning points, but see below for more on that subject. If you needed to locate the stationary points precisely you could differentiate; then solving $\frac{dy}{dx} = 0$ would tell you that there are only two turning points, at $x = 0$ and at $x = -4$.

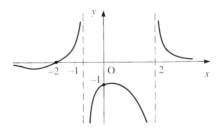

Figure 6.6

How many turning points?

You based your sketch of $y = \dfrac{x+2}{(x-2)(x+1)}$

on the information shown here in figure 6.7(a).

(a)

Can you be sure that there are only two turning points, as you chose to sketch it – see figure 6.7(b)?

(b)
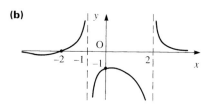

How do you know that figure 6.7(c), with additional turning points, is wrong?

To answer these questions you need to look at two ways you could solve the equation $Y = \dfrac{x+2}{(x-2)(x+1)}$ where Y is a given value.

(c)
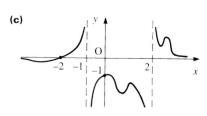

(i) You could draw graphs and observe where the horizontal line $y = Y$ meets the curve $y = \dfrac{x+2}{(x-2)(x+1)}$.

Figure 6.7

(ii) Alternatively, you could multiply both sides by $(x-2)(x+1)$, getting

$$(x-2)(x+1)Y = x+2$$

which is a quadratic equation in x (unless $Y = 0$).

It may have

● no roots, corresponding to line A (figure 6.8) not meeting the curve;

● or one root (i.e. repeated roots) – see line B;

● or two distinct roots – see lines C and D.

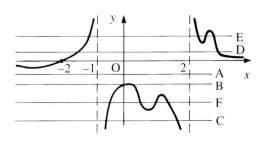

Figure 6.8

The quadratic equation cannot have more than two roots: a horizontal line cannot meet the curve in more than two places. But lines E and F each meet the curve four times, a clear contradiction.

You already know you have a (local) maximum between $x = -1$ and $x = 2$ and a (local) minimum to the left of $x = -2$. Each additional turning point increases (by 2) the number of times the curve meets a horizontal line which already intersects the curve. So you cannot have additional turning points.

Incidentally, this argument also tells you that the maximum must be lower than the minimum.

ACTIVITY

Sketch the graph of

(i) $y = \dfrac{3x - 6}{(x + 2)(x - 3)}$;

(ii) $y = \dfrac{x - 2}{(x - 1)^2}$.

In **(ii)** be careful about what happens near the vertical asymptote.

When you examined the behaviour of $y = \dfrac{x + 2}{(x - 2)(x + 1)}$ as x tends to infinity, you divided numerator and denominator by the highest power of x. A similar argument shows that if the numerator of a rational function is of lower degree than the denominator then $y = 0$ is a horizontal asymptote. If the numerator has the same degree as the denominator, you can use the same method, as in the following example, but notice how you get more information if you divide the numerator by the denominator first.

EXAMPLE 6.1

Sketch the graph of $y = \dfrac{(x - 2)(6 - x)}{(x + 1)(x - 4)}$.

SOLUTION

$$y = \frac{(x - 2)(6 - x)}{(x + 1)(x - 4)}$$

$$= \frac{-x^2 + 8x - 12}{x^2 - 3x - 4}$$

$$= \frac{-1 + \dfrac{8}{x} - \dfrac{12}{x^2}}{1 - \dfrac{3}{x} - \dfrac{4}{x^2}}$$ ← Dividing top and bottom by x^2

which tends to -1 as $x \to \pm\infty$, indicating that the line $y = -1$ is a horizontal asymptote.

133

Dividing the numerator $(-x^2 + 8x - 12)$ by the denominator $(x^2 - 3x - 4)$, you get

$$y = -1 + \frac{5x - 16}{(x + 1)(x - 4)}.$$

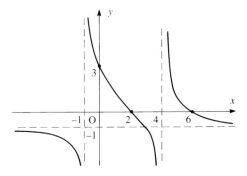

When x is large and positive $(5x - 16)$, $(x + 1)$ and $(x - 4)$ are positive so that y is slightly more than -1; we say: $y \to -1$ from above as $x \to +\infty$.

When x is numerically large but negative these three terms are negative so that y is slightly less than -1; we say: $y \to -1$ from below as $x \to -\infty$.

(Alternatively, evaluate y for numerically large x, such as $x = 100$ and $x = -100$).

The graph cuts the y axis at $(0, 3)$, and the x axis at $(2, 0)$ and at $(6, 0)$. The vertical asymptotes are $x = -1$ and $x = 4$.

As $x \to -1$ from the left, $y \to -\infty$; as $x \to -1$ from the right, $y \to +\infty$.
As $x \to 4$ from the left, $y \to -\infty$; as $x \to 4$ from the right, $y \to +\infty$.

All this information is included in figure 6.9.

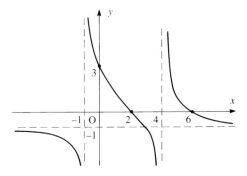

Figure 6.9

The equation $y = \dfrac{(x - 2)(6 - x)}{(x + 1)(x - 4)}$ is equivalent to a quadratic in x, so each horizontal line (except the asymptote $y = -1$) will cross the graph at most twice. There cannot be any stationary points.

In Example 6.1 the information about the behaviour near the vertical asymptotes was in fact superfluous: you could have drawn your sketch using only the intercepts and the behaviour as $x \to \infty$. It did, however, provide confirmation that the sketch was correct.

Recognising symmetry can help you to draw a sketch. If $f(x) = f(-x)$ the graph of $y = f(x)$ is symmetrical about the y axis, and f is an *even* function – see *Pure Mathematics 2*, page 94; functions containing only even powers of x are even functions. If $f(x) = -f(-x)$ the graph of $y = f(x)$ has rotational symmetry of order 2 about the origin; in this case f is an *odd* function.

EXAMPLE 6.2

Sketch the graph of $y = \mathrm{f}(x)$, where $\mathrm{f}(x) = \dfrac{x^2 + 1}{x^2 + 2}$.

SOLUTION

When $x = 0$, $y = \frac{1}{2}$ so the graph passes through $\left(0, \frac{1}{2}\right)$.

No (real) value of x makes $x^2 + 1 = 0$, so the graph does not cut the x axis.

No (real) value of x makes $x^2 + 2 = 0$, so there are no vertical asymptotes.

Now $y = \dfrac{x^2 + 1}{x^2 + 2} = 1 - \dfrac{1}{x^2 + 2}$ so $y \to 1$ from below as $x \to \pm\infty$.

As $\mathrm{f}(x)$ contains only even powers of x, f is an even function and the graph is symmetrical about the y axis (see figure 6.10).

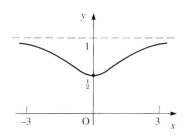

Figure 6.10

Symmetry considerations tell you that the graph is stationary at $\left(0, \frac{1}{2}\right)$.

As $y = \dfrac{x^2 + 1}{x^2 + 2}$ is effectively a quadratic equation in x, no horizontal line will cross the graph more than twice, so you cannot have any other turning points. (Differentiation will also confirm that $\left(0, \frac{1}{2}\right)$ is the only stationary point.)

As shown in the next example, a somewhat similar approach allows you to deal with rational functions with numerator of higher degree than denominator.

EXAMPLE 6.3

Sketch the graph of $y = \dfrac{x^2 - 2}{x - 1}$.

SOLUTION

Dividing numerator by denominator we get

$$y = \frac{x^2 - 2}{x - 1}$$

$$= x + 1 - \frac{1}{x - 1}.$$

Since $\dfrac{1}{x - 1} \to 0$ as $x \to \pm\infty$, when x is numerically large y is approximately $x + 1$; thus the graph of $y = \dfrac{x^2 - 2}{x - 1}$ approaches the line $y = x + 1$ asymptotically as $x \to \pm\infty$. The line $y = x + 1$ is an oblique asymptote.

When x is large and positive the graph of $y = \dfrac{x^2 - 2}{x - 1}$ is just below $y = x + 1$;

when x is numerically large but negative the graph of $y = \dfrac{x^2 - 2}{x - 1}$ is slightly above $y = x + 1$.

The graph cuts the x axis when $x = \pm\sqrt{2}$ (i.e. when $x \approx \pm1.41$). The vertical asymptote is $x = 1$, with $y \to +\infty$ as $x \to 1$ from the left and $y \to -\infty$ as $x \to 1$ from the right.

The graph is as sketched in figure 6.11.

There are no stationary points as $y = \dfrac{x^2 - 2}{x - 1}$ is effectively a quadratic equation in x, so that horizontal lines can cut the curve at most twice.

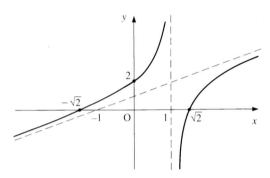

Figure 6.11

Sketch the graphs in Questions 1–18.

1 $y = \dfrac{2}{x - 3}$

2 $y = \dfrac{2}{(x - 3)^2}$

3 $y = \dfrac{x - 5}{(x + 2)(x - 3)}$

4 $y = \dfrac{3 - x}{(2 - x)(4 - x)}$

5 $y = \dfrac{x}{x^2 - 4}$

6 $y = \dfrac{x - 3}{(x - 4)^2}$

7 $y = \dfrac{x^2(x - 2)}{x^2 - 1}$

8 $y = \dfrac{(2x - 3)(5x + 2)}{(x + 1)(x - 4)}$

9 $y = \dfrac{x(x - 1)}{x + 1}$

10 $y = \dfrac{x^2 + 3}{x - 2}$

11 $y = \dfrac{(x - 4)(x - 1)}{x - 2}$

12 $y = \dfrac{1}{x^2 + 1}$

13 $y = \dfrac{x}{x^2 + 3}$

14 $y = \dfrac{4 - x^2}{4 + x^2}$

15 $y = \dfrac{x^3 - 8}{x^2 + 1}$

16 $y = \dfrac{x^3 + 1}{x - 1}$

17 $y = \dfrac{x^2 - 6x + 9}{x^2 + 1}$

18 $y = \dfrac{x^2 - 5x - 6}{(x + 1)(x - 4)}$

Hammum Plot.   [Be careful!]

19 The concentration y of a drug in the blood x hours after it has been administered is modelled by $y = \dfrac{x}{20x^2 + 50x + 80}$. Sketch the graph for $x \geqslant 0$. When does the maximum concentration occur?

20 Describe the symmetry of the graph of $y = \dfrac{x^4 - x^2 + 2}{x^4 + 1}$ and locate its asymptotes. Sketch the graph.

21 The police use a radar 'gun' to measure the speed of approaching vehicles. The gun is both transmitter and receiver, transmitting at frequency f (usually about 10 GHz) and receiving part of the radar beam reflected from the moving vehicle. The gun measures b, the difference in the frequencies of the transmitted and reflected beams. The speed u of the vehicle is modelled by $u = \dfrac{cb}{b + f}$, where c is the speed of light, about 3×10^8 ms^{-1}. Sketch the graph of u against b. What difference does it make to the gradient of the relevant part of the graph if the police decrease the value of f?

22 When a camera with lens of focal length F mm and aperture f is focused on an object which is d mm from the camera other objects may also appear acceptably sharp. The region of acceptable sharpness is known as the *depth of field*. The near limit of the depth of field is d_{near} mm and the far limit (if there is one) is d_{far} mm, where

$$d_{near} = \frac{d}{1 + \dfrac{0.025df}{F^2}} \quad \text{and} \quad d_{far} = \frac{d}{1 - \dfrac{0.025df}{F^2}} \quad \text{(provided } F^2 > 0.025df\text{)}.$$

The aperture f is usually one of the numbers 1.4, 2, 2.8, 4, 5.6, 8, 11, 16, 22, ... where a large number represents a small aperture, and vice versa. Sketch d_{near} and d_{far} against positive f, for fixed d, taking $F = 50$.

Explain why landscape photographers frequently choose a small aperture, while portrait photographers often choose a comparatively large aperture.

23 Sketch the graph of $y = \dfrac{x}{x^2 - 9}$.

(i) Show how the equation can be rearranged as a quadratic equation in x, provided $y \neq 0$.

(ii) If y is given (and is not 0), how many values of x can be found?

(iii) The graph is continuous for x between -3 and 3. What happens to y as x varies from -3 to 3? Explain why there are no turning points between $x = -3$ and $x = 3$.

(iv) Explain why the graph has no turning points anywhere.

24 Without using calculus explain why the graph of $y = \dfrac{x - 2}{x + 3}$ has no turning points.

25 Show that $y = \dfrac{(x - b)}{(x - a)(x - c)}$ has no turning points if $a < b < c$. What happens if $a = c$ and $b < a$?

Graphs of $y^2 = f(x)$

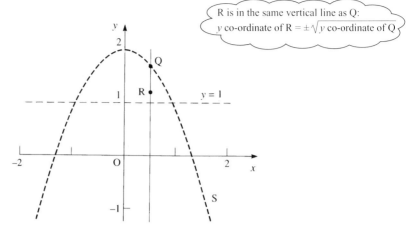

Figure 6.12

In figure 6.12, the dashed curve (labelled S) is the graph of $y = 2 - x^2$.

(i) Copy the diagram, mark (fairly accurately) several possible positions for R, and sketch the locus of R as Q moves along curve S.

(ii) Describe the position of R relative to Q when the y co-ordinate of R is positive and
   (a) Q is above the line $y = 1$;
   (b) Q is on the line $y = 1$;
   (c) Q is between the x axis and the line $y = 1$.

(iii) What happens when Q is below the x axis?

(iv) Explain why the locus of R is a complete circle.

The locus of R constructed in the activity above is the circle with equation $y^2 = 2 - x^2$. It is symmetrical about the x axis, a property of all curves representing equations of the form $y^2 = f(x)$. This is because if (x_1, y_1) satisfies $y^2 = f(x)$, then $(x_1, -y_1)$ also satisfies the equation. Notice, too, that the graph only exists for values of x which make $f(x) \geq 0$.

The curve representing $y^2 = f(x)$ can cross the x axis in a number of ways. We illustrate two of these in the following example.

EXAMPLE 6.4

Sketch curve C, the graph of $y^2 = x^2(x + 2)$.

SOLUTION

First sketch the graph of $y = x^2(x + 2)$ obtaining curve S, shown dashed in figure 6.13. Each point (such as Q) on S above the x axis gives rise to two points (R and R′) on C, symmetrically arranged about the x axis: R is always nearer to $y = 1$ than Q, and R′ is the image of R by reflection in the x axis.

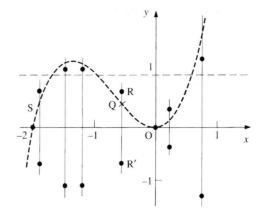

Figure 6.13

As S intersects the x axis at $(-2, 0)$ and at $(0, 0)$, C also intersects the x axis at these points. Now look more carefully at the gradient of C at these two points:

$$y^2 = x^2(x + 2) \Longrightarrow y = \pm x \sqrt{x + 2}$$

$$\Longrightarrow \frac{\mathrm{d}y}{\mathrm{d}x} = \pm \left[\sqrt{x + 2} + x \cdot \frac{1}{2}(x + 2)^{-\frac{1}{2}} \right]$$

Using the product and chain rules

$$\Longrightarrow \frac{\mathrm{d}y}{\mathrm{d}x} = \pm \left(\sqrt{x + 2} + \frac{x}{2\sqrt{x + 2}} \right).$$

As $x \to -2$ from the right, $\frac{\mathrm{d}y}{\mathrm{d}x} \to \pm\infty$ so that at $(-2, 0)$ the tangent to C is parallel to the y axis.

However at $(0, 0)$, $\frac{\mathrm{d}y}{\mathrm{d}x} \to \pm\sqrt{2}$ so we complete the sketch as shown in figure 6.14.

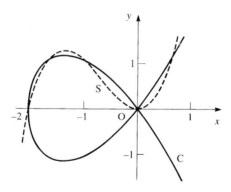

Figure 6.14

Alternatively, you could use the fact that near the origin

$$y^2 = x^2(x + 2) \quad \Longrightarrow \quad y^2 \approx 2x^2 \quad \Longrightarrow \quad y \approx \pm\sqrt{2}x.$$

Differentiating the general equation $y^2 = f(x)$ with respect to x gives

$$2y \frac{dy}{dx} = f'(x).$$

If the curve C with equation $y^2 = f(x)$ meets the x axis at the point $P(x_1, 0)$ two possibilities arise:

either $f'(x_1) \neq 0$ in which case the tangent to C at P is parallel to the y axis, as at $(-2, 0)$ in Example 6.4;

or $f'(x_1) = 0$ in which case the direction of the tangent at P depends on the particular function f. You will need to treat each such case separately.

Thus the curve C representing $y^2 = f(x)$ crosses the x axis at $(x_1, 0)$ where $f(x_1) = 0$; the tangent to C at the point $(x_1, 0)$ is vertical unless $f'(x_1) = 0$.

EXERCISE 6B

Sketch the graphs in Questions 1–6.

1 $y^2 = (x + 2)(x - 1)(x - 4)$

2 $y^2 = \frac{1}{12} x^3(4 - x)$

3 $y^2 = x^4(x + 2)$

4 $y^2 = \frac{x}{1 + x^2}$

5 $y^2 = \frac{x^2}{x^2 - 1}$

6 $y^2 = \frac{x^2 - 1}{x^2 - 4}$

7 Sketch the graph of the equation $y^2 = x^3$. This is known as the *semi-cubical parabola*.

8 On one set of axes sketch the graphs of $y^2 = 3x - x^3 + c$ for $c = 4, 2, 0, -2, -4$.

9 A curve has equation $y = x + 2 + \frac{4}{x - 3}$.

(i) Calculate the co-ordinates of the points where the curve crosses the y axis and the x axis.

(ii) Find $\frac{dy}{dx}$, and hence calculate the co-ordinates of the two stationary points on the curve.

(iii) Explain how the curve is related to the line $y = x + 2$.

(iv) Sketch the curve, together with its asymptotes.

(v) On a separate diagram, sketch the curve with equation

$$y^2 = x + 2 + \frac{4}{x - 3}.$$

Indicate clearly the co-ordinates of the points where this curve crosses the axes, and the stationary points.

[MEI]

10 A curve has equation $y = \dfrac{(4x + 1)(x + 16)}{x^2 + 4}$.

   (i) Show that y can be expressed in the form $A + \dfrac{Bx}{x^2 + 4}$, stating the values of A and B. Write down the equation of the asymptote parallel to the x axis.

   (ii) Find $\dfrac{dy}{dx}$, and hence calculate the co-ordinates of the two stationary points.

   (iii) Sketch the curve.

   (iv) On a separate diagram, sketch the curve with equation

$$y^2 = \frac{(4x + 1)(x + 16)}{x^2 + 4}.$$

[In **(iii)** and **(iv)**, you should give the co-ordinates of the points where these curves cross the axes and the co-ordinates of the stationary points.]

[MEI]

11 A curve has equation $y = \dfrac{x^2 - 1}{(2x + a)^2}$ where a is a constant such that $a > 2$.

   (i) Write down the co-ordinates of the points where the curve crosses the axes, and write down the equations of the two asymptotes.

   (ii) Find $\dfrac{dy}{dx}$, and hence show that the stationary point on the curve is $\left(-\dfrac{2}{a}, -\dfrac{1}{a^2 - 4}\right)$.

   (iii) Sketch the curve.

   (iv) On a separate diagram, sketch the curve with equation $y^2 = \dfrac{x^2 - 1}{(2x + a)^2}$.

[MEI]

Graphs of $y = |f(x)|$

When sketching the graph of $y = |2 - x^2|$ it is again helpful to start by sketching the curve S with equation $y = 2 - x^2$. As $|n| = -n$ if $n < 0$, any part of S which is below the x axis is reflected in the x axis to form part of the graph of $y = |2 - x^2|$ (see figure 6.15); any part of S which is above the x axis forms part of the graph of $y = |2 - x^2|$ without alteration.

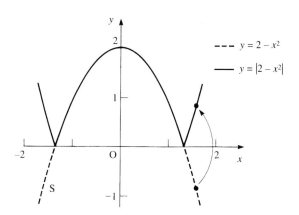

Figure 6.15

EXAMPLE 6.5

Sketch the graph of $y = \left| \dfrac{x+2}{(x-2)(x+1)} \right|$.

SOLUTION

You developed the sketch of $y = \dfrac{x+2}{(x-2)(x+1)}$ in figure 6.6 on page 131.

It is shown again here: sections which are above the x axis have been drawn with a continuous curve, while sections which are below the x axis have been drawn dashed.

The dashed sections (below the x axis) are reflected in the x axis, the image being drawn with a continuous curve.

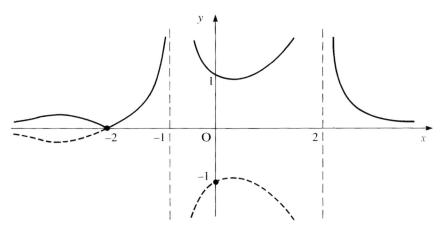

Figure 6.16

The graph of $y = \left| \dfrac{x+2}{(x-2)(x+1)} \right|$ is shown by the continuous curve above.

It should be noted that at $(-2, 0)$ the curve is cusped and not smooth.

EXERCISE 6C

Sketch the graphs in Questions 1–6.

1 $y = |x(x-1)(x-2)|$

2 $y = \left| \dfrac{x}{x+1} \right|$

3 $y = \left| \dfrac{1-x^2}{x^2-4} \right|$

4 $y = \left| \dfrac{x-1}{x^2+1} \right|$

5 $y = |\sin x|$

6 $y = \left| \dfrac{x(x-1)}{x-2} \right|$

7 On the same axes sketch the graphs of $y = \left| \dfrac{1}{2+x} \right|$ and $y = \left| \dfrac{x}{x-5} \right|$.

How many roots does the equation $\left| \dfrac{1}{2+x} \right| = \left| \dfrac{x}{x-5} \right|$ have?

8 Sketch the curve whose equation is $y = f(x) = \dfrac{(x-4)(x-1)}{x(x-5)}$ stating the equations of its asymptotes. Find the co-ordinates of any stationary points and explain how their nature might be determined. Sketch on separate diagrams the curves with equations

(i) $y^2 = f(x)$

(ii) $y = |f(x)|$.

[MEI]

9 The equation of a curve is $y = \dfrac{6x - 2x^2}{x^2 + 3}$.

(i) Find $\dfrac{dy}{dx}$, simplifying your answer.

(ii) Show that the x co-ordinates of the two stationary points satisfy the equation

$$3 - 2x - x^2 = 0$$

and find the co-ordinates of the stationary points.

(iii) State the equation of the horizontal asymptote.

(iv) Sketch the curve. Your sketch should show clearly the stationary points, the asymptote, and the points where the curve crosses the axes.

(v) On a separate diagram, sketch the graph with equation $y = \left| \dfrac{6x - 2x^2}{x^2 + 3} \right|$.

(vi) Solve the equation $\left| \dfrac{6x - 2x^2}{x^2 + 3} \right| = 2$.

[MEI]

Inequalities

An *inequality* is a statement involving one of the order relationships $<, >, \leqslant, \geqslant$. There are two types of inequality:

- those whose truth depends on the value of the variable involved

- those which are always true.

For example: the statement $x^2 > 4$ is true if and only if $x < -2$ or $x > 2$,

whereas the statement $(x - 3)^2 + y^2 \geqslant 0$ is true for all real values of x and y.

This section deals with the first type of inequality, in which the task is to find the set of values for which the inequality is true; this is called *solving the inequality*.

The basic statement $x > y$ can be interpreted in two simple ways:

$x > y \iff$ the point representing x is to the right of the point representing y on the standard number line;

$x > y \iff x - y$ is positive.

Either interpretation can be used to justify the familiar basic rules for manipulating inequalities.

Rule	Example (based on 'is greater than')
1 You may add the same number to each side of an inequality	$x > y \Leftrightarrow x + a > y + a$
2 You may multiply (or divide) both sides of an inequality by the same positive number	If p is positive: $x > y \Leftrightarrow px > py$
3 If both sides of an inequality are multiplied (or divided) by the same negative number the inequality is reversed	If n is negative: $x > y \Leftrightarrow nx < ny$
4 You may add (but not subtract) corresponding sides of inequalities of the same type	$a > b$ and $x > y \Rightarrow a + x > b + y$
5 Inequalities of the same type are *transitive*	$x > y$ and $y > z \Rightarrow x > z$

Similar definitions apply to each of the inequalities $>, <, \geqslant, \leqslant$, and the same basic rules can be proved from the definitions.

EXAMPLE 6.6

Starting from the definition that $x > y$ means that $x - y$ is positive, prove Rule 3, that if n is negative, $x > y \Leftrightarrow nx < ny$.

SOLUTION

$x > y \quad \Leftrightarrow \quad x - y$ is positive
$\qquad\quad \Leftrightarrow \quad n(x - y)$ is negative as n is negative
$\qquad\quad \Leftrightarrow \quad nx - ny$ is negative
$\qquad\quad \Leftrightarrow \quad nx < ny$.

ACTIVITY

Use the number line and/or the properties of positive and negative numbers to justify Rules 1, 2, 4 and 5. Include a counter-example to show that inequalities may not be subtracted.

An obvious method of solving an inequality such as $f(x) > 0$ is to use the graph of $y = f(x)$: the solution is then the set of values of x for which the graph is above the x axis. Similarly, when solving $g(x) \leqslant h(x)$ you could draw the graphs of $y = g(x)$ and $y = h(x)$ and find the values of x where the first graph intersects or is lower than the second graph. But unless the graphs are already drawn, or are required for another purpose, it is usually quicker to use a mixture of algebra and simpler graphs, as illustrated in the following examples.

EXAMPLE 6.7

Solve the inequality $\dfrac{x^2 - 2}{x - 1} \leqslant 0$.

SOLUTION 1

Sketch the curve $y = \dfrac{x^2 - 2}{x - 1}$, as shown here. (This graph was sketched on page 136, figure 6.11). From figure 6.17 you can see that $y \leqslant 0$ when $x \leqslant -\sqrt{2}$ or $1 < x \leqslant \sqrt{2}$.

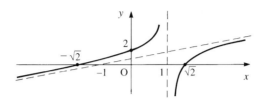

Figure 6.17

SOLUTION 2

If you want to multiply the inequality by $x - 1$, you have problems as you do not know whether $x - 1$ is positive or negative: you need to consider both possibilities. A better method is to multiply by $(x - 1)^2$, which you know is positive, obtaining $(x^2 - 2)(x - 1) \leqslant 0$, $x - 1 \neq 0$.

Now the sketch of $y = (x^2 - 2)(x - 1)$ allows you to read off the solutions (see figure 6.18).

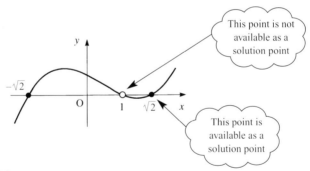

This point is not available as a solution point

This point is available as a solution point

Figure 6.18

Again you obtain $x \leqslant -\sqrt{2}$ or $1 < x \leqslant \sqrt{2}$. (Note the exclusion of $x = 1$.)

SOLUTION 3

As the value of x changes, a function $f(x)$ can only change its sign as x passes through a value where $f(x) = 0$ or where $f(x)$ is undefined. These values of x are known as *critical points*. You can solve an inequality by checking the truth of the inequality at and on either side of these critical points.

For $\dfrac{x^2 - 2}{x - 1} \leqslant 0$ the critical points are where you have equality (at $x = \pm\sqrt{2}$) and where $\dfrac{x^2 - 2}{x - 1}$ is undefined (at $x = 1$). You must now test whether the inequality is true or not in the various regions. (**Y** indicates the inequality is true.)

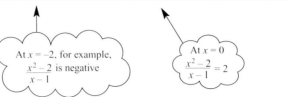

	$x < -\sqrt{2}$	$x = -\sqrt{2}$	$-\sqrt{2} < x < 1$	$x = 1$	$1 < x < \sqrt{2}$	$x = \sqrt{2}$	$x > \sqrt{2}$
$\dfrac{x^2 - 2}{x - 1} \leqslant 0$	Y	Y	N	N	Y	Y	N

At $x = -2$, for example,
$\dfrac{x^2 - 2}{x - 1}$ is negative

At $x = 0$
$\dfrac{x^2 - 2}{x - 1} = 2$

At $x = 2$
$\dfrac{x^2 - 2}{x - 1} = 2$

As before, the solution is $x \leqslant -\sqrt{2}$, or $1 < x \leqslant \sqrt{2}$.

When solving an inequality which involves two functions, such as $f(x) \leqslant g(x)$, it is usually good practice to rearrange it in the equivalent form $f(x) - g(x) \leqslant 0$, as in Example 6.8.

EXAMPLE 6.8   Solve the inequality $\dfrac{2x - 1}{x - 1} \leqslant \dfrac{9}{x + 1}$.

SOLUTION

Provided $x \neq \pm 1$

Multiply by
$(x - 1)^2(x + 1)^2$,
which is positive

$$\frac{2x - 1}{x - 1} \leqslant \frac{9}{x + 1} \Leftrightarrow \frac{2x - 1}{x - 1} - \frac{9}{x + 1} \leqslant 0$$

$$\Leftrightarrow (2x - 1)(x + 1)^2(x - 1) - 9(x - 1)^2(x + 1) \leqslant 0$$

$$\Leftrightarrow (x + 1)(x - 1)[(2x - 1)(x + 1) - 9(x - 1)] \leqslant 0$$

$$\Leftrightarrow (x + 1)(x - 1)(2x^2 - 8x + 8) \leqslant 0$$

$$\Leftrightarrow 2(x + 1)(x - 1)(x - 2)^2 \leqslant 0$$

A sketch of $y = 2(x + 1)(x - 1)(x - 2)^2$ gives you the solution $-1 < x < 1$ or $x = 2$.

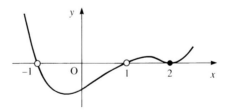

Figure 6.19

When solving inequalities involving modulus signs you can make use of the equivalents

$$|f(x)| \leqslant p \quad \Leftrightarrow \quad -p \leqslant f(x) \leqslant p \quad \Leftrightarrow \quad (f(x))^2 \leqslant p^2$$

but it is often simpler to use graphs.

EXAMPLE 6.9   Solve $3\,|x-2| > x+2$.

SOLUTION

The graph of $y = 3\,|x-2|$ consists of half-lines with gradients 3 and -3 starting from $(2, 0)$; these and the line $y = x + 2$ are as shown in figure 6.20.

It is easy to verify that the points of intersection are $(1, 3)$ and $(4, 6)$. The solution of the inequality is $x < 1$ or $x > 4$.

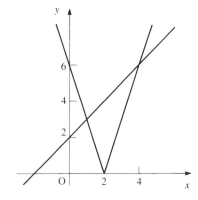

Figure 6.20

EXAMPLE 6.10   Solve the inequality $\left|\dfrac{x+3}{x-1}\right| \leqslant 2$.

SOLUTION 1

$$\left|\frac{x+3}{x-1}\right| \leqslant 2 \quad \Longleftrightarrow \quad -2 \leqslant \frac{x+3}{x-1} \leqslant 2.$$

Then, provided $x \neq 1$,

$$\frac{x+3}{x-1} \leqslant 2 \qquad \text{and} \qquad \frac{x+3}{x-1} \geqslant -2$$

$\Longleftrightarrow \quad (x+3)(x-1) - 2(x-1)^2 \leqslant 0$ 　　　$\Longleftrightarrow \quad (x+3)(x-1) + 2(x-1)^2 \geqslant 0$

$\Longleftrightarrow \quad (x-1)[(x+3) - 2(x-1)] \leqslant 0$ 　　$\Longleftrightarrow \quad (x-1)[(x+3) + 2(x-1)] \geqslant 0$

$\Longleftrightarrow \quad (x-1)(-x+5) \leqslant 0$ 　　　　　　$\Longleftrightarrow \quad (x-1)(3x+1) \geqslant 0$

$\Longleftrightarrow \quad x < 1$ or $x \geqslant 5$. 　　　　　　　$\Longleftrightarrow \quad x \leqslant -\frac{1}{3}$ or $x > 1$.

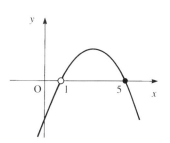   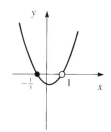

Figure 6.21

You want the values of x which satisfy both inequalities: the solution is $x \leqslant -\frac{1}{3}$ or $x \geqslant 5$.

SOLUTION 2

The same answer can be obtained more easily if you use the fact that

$$|f(x)| < k \iff (f(x))^2 \leqslant k^2.$$

Thus, again provided $x \neq 1$,

$$\left|\frac{x+3}{x-1}\right| \leqslant 2 \iff \left(\frac{x+3}{x-1}\right)^2 \leqslant 4$$

$$\iff (x+3)^2 - 4(x-1)^2 \leqslant 0$$

$$\iff -3x^2 + 14x + 5 \leqslant 0$$

$$\iff -(3x+1)(x-5) \leqslant 0$$

$$\iff x \leqslant -\tfrac{1}{3} \text{ or } x \geqslant 5$$

as shown in figure 6.22.

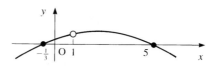

Figure 6.22

Solve the inequalities in Questions 1–15.

1 $(x+3)(x-1)(2x-7) > 0$

2 $(x-1)(x-2)^2(x-3)^3 > 0$

3 $x^3 < x(3x+10)$

4 $\dfrac{(x-5)(x-2)}{x+1} \leqslant 0$

5 $\dfrac{5x-2}{(x+1)(x-2)} \geqslant 0$

6 $\dfrac{(x+2)(x-4)}{x(x-2)^2} \geqslant 0$

7 $\dfrac{x^2-2}{x-3} < 2$

8 $\dfrac{x^3-4}{x-2} \leqslant x+2$

9 $\dfrac{2x+3}{x-2} \leqslant 1$

10 $\dfrac{1}{x+6} \leqslant \dfrac{2}{2-3x}$

11 $|x+1| \geqslant |5-3x|$

12 $\left|\dfrac{2x+3}{x-2}\right| \leqslant 1$

13 $|2x-1| < 3x-1$

14 $\left|\dfrac{(x-1)(x-5)}{x-3}\right| \leqslant 3$

15 $\left|\dfrac{5-3x}{x+1}\right| \leqslant 1$

16 **(i)** Solve the inequality $(x+2)(x-3) < 4x$.

(ii) Solve the inequality $x+2 < \dfrac{4x}{x-3}$.

[MEI, part]

" You ~~were~~ ^look dirty. Would you like a shower"

17 A curve has equation $y = \dfrac{x^2 - 1}{(5x - 7)^2}$.

   (i) Write down the equation of the asymptote parallel to the y axis, and the equation of the asymptote parallel to the x axis.

   (ii) Find $\dfrac{dy}{dx}$. Hence show that there is only one stationary point, and that its co-ordinates are $\left(\dfrac{5}{7}, -\dfrac{1}{24}\right)$.

   (iii) Sketch the curve.

   (iv) On a separate diagram, sketch the curve with equation $y = \left|\dfrac{x^2 - 1}{(5x - 7)^2}\right|$.

   (v) Find the three values of x for which $\left|\dfrac{x^2 - 1}{(5x - 7)^2}\right| = \dfrac{1}{25}$, and hence solve the inequality

$$\left|\frac{x^2 - 1}{(5x - 7)^2}\right| < \frac{1}{25}.$$

[**MEI**]

18 A curve has equation $y = \dfrac{14x - 12}{x^2 - 4}$.

   (i) Find $\dfrac{dy}{dx}$ and show that there are no stationary points.

   (ii) Sketch the curve. Give the equations of the asymptotes, and the co-ordinates of the points where the curve crosses the axes.

   (iii) On a separate diagram, sketch the curve with equation $y = \left|\dfrac{14x - 12}{x^2 - 4}\right|$.

   (iv) Calculate the values of x for which $\dfrac{14x - 12}{x^2 - 4} = -3$.

   (v) Solve the inequality $\left|\dfrac{14x - 12}{x^2 - 4}\right| < 3$.

[**MEI**]

19 Rearrange $y = \dfrac{(x - 2)(x + 1)}{x^2}$ as a quadratic equation in x. (One of the coefficients will involve y.) Write down the condition for this equation to have real roots. Without using calculus, deduce the maximum value of y for real x.

20 Use the method of Question 19 to prove that, for real x,

$$1 \leqslant \frac{9x^2 + 8x + 3}{x^2 + 1} \leqslant 11.$$

21 Find the set of possible values of $\dfrac{6x + 6}{x^2 + 3}$ for real x.

22 Show that $\dfrac{x^2 - 2px + 1}{px^2 - 2x + p}$ lies between -1 and 1 provided that p is not between -1 and 1.

INVESTIGATIONS

   1 Given that a, b, c, d and k are constants, investigate

   (i) the form of the graph of $y = \dfrac{(x - a)(x - b)}{(x - c)(x - d)}$;

   (ii) the number and location of solutions of the equation

$$\frac{(x - a)(x - b)}{(x - c)(x - d)} = k.$$

2 Investigate the shape of the graph of $y = \dfrac{ax^2 + bx + c}{Ax^2 + Bx + C}$ when

(i) $b^2 < 4ac$ and $B^2 = 4AC$

(ii) $b^2 \geqslant 4ac$ and $B^2 < 4AC$

(iii) $b^2 < 4ac$ and $B^2 > 4AC$

KEY POINTS

1 A *rational function* is a function which can be expressed in the form $\dfrac{N(x)}{D(x)}$, where the numerator, $N(x)$, and denominator, $D(x)$, are polynomials, and $D(x)$ is not the zero polynomial.

2 To sketch the graph of $y = \dfrac{N(x)}{D(x)}$:

(i) Find the intercepts, that is where the graph cuts the axes.

(ii) Examine the behaviour of the graph near the vertical asymptotes; these are the lines $x = a$ if $D(a) = 0$ and $N(a) \neq 0$.

(iii) Examine the behaviour as x tends to $\pm\infty$.

(iv) Show what you have found in (i), (ii) and (iii) on a sketch graph.

(v) Complete the sketch.

3 The graph of $y^2 = |f(x)|$ is symmetrical about the x axis. If the graph crosses the x axis at $(x_1, 0)$, the tangent to the curve at that point is parallel to the y axis unless $f'(x_1) = 0$. If $f'(x_1) = 0$ give special consideration to the value of the gradient.

4 To sketch C, the graph of $y = |f(x)|$, first sketch S, the graph of $y = f(x)$: any parts of S which are above the x axis are also parts of C. Complete C by reflecting in the x axis any parts of S which are below the x axis.

5 If you want to multiply (or divide) both sides of an inequality by some number you need to know its sign:

- if p is positive: $x > y \iff px > py$

- if n is negative: $x > y \iff nx < ny$.

When multiplying or dividing by a negative number, reverse the inequality.

6 When solving inequalities involving rational functions, it can often be helpful to multiply by the square of the denominator (as this is automatically positive).

7 For positive p, these three statements are equivalent:

$$|f(x)| \leqslant p \quad -p \leqslant f(x) \leqslant p \quad (f(x))^2 \leqslant p^2$$

Appendix: the scalar triple product

This brief account of the scalar triple product tidies up some loose ends from earlier sections; a full treatment is given in *Pure Mathematics 6*.

In parallelogram OACB, the sides OA and OB are represented by vectors **a** and **b** (figure A.1).

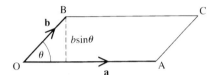

Figure A.1

The area of the parallelogram is OA × OBsinθ which is the magnitude of **a** × **b**.

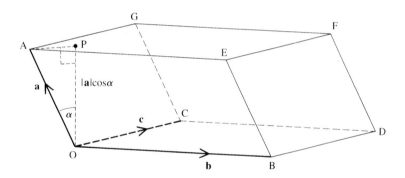

Figure A.2

A *parallelepiped* is a polyhedron with six faces each of which is a parallelogram.

The volume V of any parallelepiped is the product of the base area and the height. In parallelepiped OBDCAEFG (figure A.2) take parallelogram OBDC as the base; it has area $|\mathbf{b} \times \mathbf{c}|$. The height of the parallelepiped is OP, where P is the foot of the perpendicular from O to plane AEFG.

If angle AOP is α, the length of OP is $|\mathbf{a}|\cos\alpha$, and the volume of parallelepiped OBDCAEFG is $V = |\mathbf{a}||\mathbf{b} \times \mathbf{c}|\cos\alpha$.

If, as illustrated in figure A.2, **a, b, c** is a right-handed set of vectors, $\mathbf{b} \times \mathbf{c}$ has the same sense as $\overrightarrow{\text{OP}}$, and $|\mathbf{a}||\mathbf{b} \times \mathbf{c}|\cos\alpha = \mathbf{a}.(\mathbf{b} \times \mathbf{c})$; in this case $V = \mathbf{a}.(\mathbf{b} \times \mathbf{c})$.

However, if **a, b, c** is left-handed, **b** × **c** and $\overrightarrow{OP}$ are parallel but with opposite senses; in this case the angle between **a** and **b** × **c** is $\pi - \alpha$, which is obtuse, so that $V = |\mathbf{a}||\mathbf{b} \times \mathbf{c}|\cos\alpha = -\mathbf{a}.(\mathbf{b} \times \mathbf{c})$.

Thus **a**.(**b** × **c**) is the signed volume of the parallelepiped with edges represented by **a**, **b** and **c**.

As the volume of the parallelepiped does not depend on which parallelogram we take as the base,

$$\mathbf{a}.(\mathbf{b} \times \mathbf{c}) = \mathbf{b}.(\mathbf{c} \times \mathbf{a}) = \mathbf{c}.(\mathbf{a} \times \mathbf{b})$$
$$= -\mathbf{a}.(\mathbf{c} \times \mathbf{b}) = -\mathbf{b}.(\mathbf{a} \times \mathbf{c}) = -\mathbf{c}.(\mathbf{b} \times \mathbf{a}).$$

The scalar **a**.(**b** × **c**) is called the *scalar triple product* of **a, b, c**. Cyclic interchange of the letters does not affect the value of the scalar triple product, but non-cyclic interchange of the letters multiplies the product by −1.

You can now prove the distributive property of vector product over vector addition. Let **e** be an arbitrary unit vector. Then

$$\mathbf{e}.(\mathbf{a} \times (\mathbf{b} + \mathbf{c})) = (\mathbf{b} + \mathbf{c}).(\mathbf{e} \times \mathbf{a})$$

Cyclic interchange of the terms **e**, **a** and (**b** + **c**) in the scalar triple product

$$= \mathbf{b}.(\mathbf{e} \times \mathbf{a}) + \mathbf{c}.(\mathbf{e} \times \mathbf{a})$$

Scalar product is distributive

$$= \mathbf{e}.(\mathbf{a} \times \mathbf{b}) + \mathbf{e}.(\mathbf{a} \times \mathbf{c})$$

Cyclic interchange of terms in the scalar triple product

$$= \mathbf{e}.(\mathbf{a} \times \mathbf{b} + \mathbf{a} \times \mathbf{c}).$$

Scalar product is distributive

Since **e** is any unit vector we may replace **e** with **i**:

$$\mathbf{i}.(\mathbf{a} \times (\mathbf{b} + \mathbf{c})) = \mathbf{i}.(\mathbf{a} \times \mathbf{b} + \mathbf{a} \times \mathbf{c}).$$

This means that the **i** components of the two vectors **a** × (**b** + **c**) and **a** × **b** + **a** × **c** are equal. A similar argument shows that the **j** components of **a** × (**b** + **c**) and **a** × **b** + **a** × **c** are equal, and that their **k** components are also equal. Thus

$$\mathbf{a} \times (\mathbf{b} + \mathbf{c}) = \mathbf{a} \times \mathbf{b} + \mathbf{a} \times \mathbf{c}.$$

In Chapter 5 you met the determinant, det **M**, of the 2 × 2 matrix $\mathbf{M} = \begin{pmatrix} a & c \\ b & d \end{pmatrix}$; det **M** = $ad - bc$, the (signed) area scale factor of the transformation represented by matrix **M**. This transformation (figure A.3) maps the unit square into parallelogram OPQR, where $\overrightarrow{OP} = \begin{pmatrix} a \\ b \end{pmatrix}$ and $\overrightarrow{OR} = \begin{pmatrix} c \\ d \end{pmatrix}$.

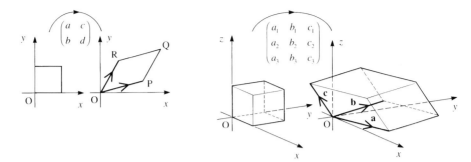

Figure A.3

In just the same way the 3×3 matrix $\mathbf{N} = \begin{pmatrix} a_1 & b_1 & c_1 \\ a_2 & b_2 & c_2 \\ a_3 & b_3 & c_3 \end{pmatrix}$ transforms the unit

cube into a parallelepiped with edges given by vectors

$$\mathbf{a} = \begin{pmatrix} a_1 \\ a_2 \\ a_3 \end{pmatrix} \quad \mathbf{b} = \begin{pmatrix} b_1 \\ b_2 \\ b_3 \end{pmatrix} \quad \mathbf{c} = \begin{pmatrix} c_1 \\ c_2 \\ c_3 \end{pmatrix}.$$

The scalar $\mathbf{a}.(\mathbf{b} \times \mathbf{c})$ is the (signed) volume of this parallelepiped; this is defined as the determinant of the 3×3 matrix $\mathbf{N}$, and is denoted by both

$\det \mathbf{N}$ and $\begin{vmatrix} a_1 & b_1 & c_1 \\ a_2 & b_2 & c_2 \\ a_3 & b_3 & c_3 \end{vmatrix}$. Therefore

$$\det \mathbf{N} = \begin{vmatrix} a_1 & b_1 & c_1 \\ a_2 & b_2 & c_2 \\ a_3 & b_3 & c_3 \end{vmatrix} = \mathbf{a}.(\mathbf{b} \times \mathbf{c})$$

$$= \begin{pmatrix} a_1 \\ a_2 \\ a_3 \end{pmatrix}.\left(\begin{pmatrix} b_1 \\ b_2 \\ b_3 \end{pmatrix} \times \begin{pmatrix} c_1 \\ c_2 \\ c_3 \end{pmatrix} \right)$$

$$= \begin{pmatrix} a_1 \\ a_2 \\ a_3 \end{pmatrix}.\left(\begin{vmatrix} b_2 & c_2 \\ b_3 & c_3 \end{vmatrix} \mathbf{i} - \begin{vmatrix} b_1 & c_1 \\ b_3 & c_3 \end{vmatrix} \mathbf{j} + \begin{vmatrix} b_1 & c_1 \\ b_2 & c_2 \end{vmatrix} \mathbf{k} \right)$$

$$= a_1 \begin{vmatrix} b_2 & c_2 \\ b_3 & c_3 \end{vmatrix} - a_2 \begin{vmatrix} b_1 & c_1 \\ b_3 & c_3 \end{vmatrix} + a_3 \begin{vmatrix} b_1 & c_1 \\ b_2 & c_2 \end{vmatrix}.$$

The expansion of the 3×3 determinant in terms of 2×2 determinants has a form similar to the expression for $\mathbf{a} \times \mathbf{b}$ in terms of 2×2 determinants. For this reason the vector product is sometimes written in the form of a 3×3 determinant:

$$\mathbf{a} \times \mathbf{b} = \begin{pmatrix} a_1 \\ a_2 \\ a_3 \end{pmatrix} \times \begin{pmatrix} b_1 \\ b_2 \\ b_3 \end{pmatrix} = \begin{vmatrix} \mathbf{i} & a_1 & b_1 \\ \mathbf{j} & a_2 & b_2 \\ \mathbf{k} & a_3 & b_3 \end{vmatrix}.$$

Evaluate the determinant $\begin{vmatrix} 2 & -1 & -2 \\ 3 & 7 & 6 \\ 5 & 4 & 9 \end{vmatrix}$.

SOLUTION

$$\begin{vmatrix} 2 & -1 & -2 \\ 3 & 7 & 6 \\ 5 & 4 & 9 \end{vmatrix} = 2\begin{vmatrix} 7 & 6 \\ 4 & 9 \end{vmatrix} - 3\begin{vmatrix} -1 & -2 \\ 4 & 9 \end{vmatrix} + 5\begin{vmatrix} -1 & -2 \\ 7 & 6 \end{vmatrix}$$

$$= 2(7 \times 9 - 4 \times 6) - 3[(-1) \times 9 - 4 \times (-2)] + 5[(-1) \times 6 - 7 \times (-2)]$$

$$= 2 \times 39 - 3 \times (-1) + 5 \times 8$$

$$= 121.$$

❓ Are the brackets in the scalar triple product $\mathbf{a}.(\mathbf{b} \times \mathbf{c})$ necessary?

1 Evaluate

(i) $\begin{vmatrix} 2 & 3 & 4 \\ 1 & 2 & 1 \\ 3 & 5 & 3 \end{vmatrix}$ (ii) $\begin{vmatrix} 1 & 4 & 3 \\ 1 & -2 & -4 \\ -5 & 3 & 7 \end{vmatrix}$

(iii) $\begin{vmatrix} 1 & 4 & 7 \\ 2 & 5 & 8 \\ 3 & 6 & 9 \end{vmatrix}$ (iv) $\begin{vmatrix} 5 & 5 & -1 \\ 3 & 0 & 2 \\ 1 & -3 & 1 \end{vmatrix}$

2 (i) Show that $\mathbf{a}.(\mathbf{b} \times \mathbf{c}) = 0 \Leftrightarrow$ O, A, B, C are coplanar.

(ii) Show that P(2, −7, 0), Q(8, −6, 4), R(−3, 38, 5) and the origin are coplanar.

(iii) Decide whether W(4, 1, 1), X(3, −3, −2), Y(2, 0, −3) and Z(5, −2, 2) are coplanar.

3 P and Q are the points (2, 5, 1) and (4, 3, 2) respectively. R and S are further points such that PQRS is a parallelogram with $\overrightarrow{QR} = -\mathbf{i} + 2\mathbf{j} + 3\mathbf{k}$. Find the co-ordinates of R and S and the area of PQRS.

4 (i) Explain why the area of triangle ABC is $\frac{1}{2}|(\mathbf{c} - \mathbf{a}) \times (\mathbf{b} - \mathbf{a})|$.

(ii) Show that the formula in part (i) simplifies to $\frac{1}{2}|\mathbf{a} \times \mathbf{b} + \mathbf{b} \times \mathbf{c} + \mathbf{c} \times \mathbf{a}|$.

(iii) Use the formula in part (i) to find the area of the triangle which has vertices at A(−3, −2), B(5, 1) and C(−6, 3).

[**Hint:** Work in three dimensions taking (−3, −2) as (−3, −2, 0).]

(iv) Check your answer to part (iii) by finding the area of the surrounding rectangle and subtracting the area of three right-angled triangles (see the diagram).

(v) Explain why it is usually easier to use the formula in part (i) rather than the formula in part (ii).

5 Show that $\mathbf{a} + \mathbf{b} + \mathbf{c} = 0 \Rightarrow \mathbf{a} \times \mathbf{b} = \mathbf{b} \times \mathbf{c} = \mathbf{c} \times \mathbf{a}$. Is the converse true?

1 Redefine a vector as an $n \times 1$ matrix. You now also need to redefine properties such as magnitude and scalar product, and some of these lose their obvious physical significance.

   (i)   Suggest possible definitions for magnitude and scalar product of

   vectors like $\begin{pmatrix} 2 \\ 2 \\ 4 \\ 1 \end{pmatrix}$.

   (ii) Find the angle between the vectors $\begin{pmatrix} 2 \\ 2 \\ 4 \\ 1 \end{pmatrix}$ and $\begin{pmatrix} 2 \\ 3 \\ -8 \\ 2 \end{pmatrix}$.

   (iii) Investigate vectors which are perpendicular both to $\begin{pmatrix} 2 \\ 2 \\ 4 \\ 1 \end{pmatrix}$ and $\begin{pmatrix} 2 \\ 3 \\ -8 \\ 2 \end{pmatrix}$.

2 The *vector triple product* of $\mathbf{a}, \mathbf{b}$ and $\mathbf{c}$ is the vector $\mathbf{a} \times (\mathbf{b} \times \mathbf{c})$.
   Is $\mathbf{a} \times (\mathbf{b} \times \mathbf{c}) = (\mathbf{a} \times \mathbf{b}) \times \mathbf{c}$?

   Investigate other properties of the vector triple product.

Answers

Chapter 1

❓ (Page 6)

Criminal proof is 'beyond reasonable doubt'. Civil proof is 'on the balance of probabilities'. Similarly, different degrees of certainty are needed in different fields: high in medical research, lower in economics. Probabilities are now often stated in weather forecasting. None of these uses absolute proof in the mathematical sense.

Activity (Page 6)

$3, 7, 31, 211, 2311, 30\,031 = 59 \times 509$

Exercise 1A (Page 9)

1 (i) $\Rightarrow$
  (ii) $\Leftarrow$
  (iii) $\Leftarrow$
  (iv) $\Leftrightarrow$
  (v) $\Rightarrow$
  (vi) $\Leftrightarrow$

2 (i) correct
  (ii) Q only if P
  (iii) P if S
  (iv) R if and only if P
  (v) correct
  (vi) Q only if R.

3 I did not have to go to school.

4 (i) For a polynomial P(x), if ($x - a$) is a factor of P(x) then P(a) = 0. True.
  (ii) If a solid has a uniform cross-section then the solid is a prism. False (e.g. twisted prism).
  (iii) If $a^2 = b^2 + c^2$ then triangle ABC has a right angle at A. True.
  (iv) If $\dfrac{\mathrm{d}y}{\mathrm{d}x} = nx^{n-1}$ then $y = x^n$. False (e.g. $y = x^n + 1$).

5 5

6 No solution

7 $(3k \pm 1)^2 = 3(3k^2 \pm 2k) + 1$, which is not a multiple of 3.

9 (i) If not then rational + irrational = rational, so irrational = rational – rational = rational. Contradiction.
  (ii) Counter-example: $(3 - \sqrt{2}) + \sqrt{2} = 3$, which is rational
  (iii) Proof as in **(i)** with $\times$ and $\div$ in place of + and –.
  (iv) Counter example: $\sqrt{2} \times \sqrt{8} = 4$.

13 (i) Show that at least three of the segments ending at a particular point are of the same colour. Consider the triangle formed by joining the other end points of three such segments.
  (ii) Green pentagon with yellow diagonals.

Chapter 2

Activity (Page 13)

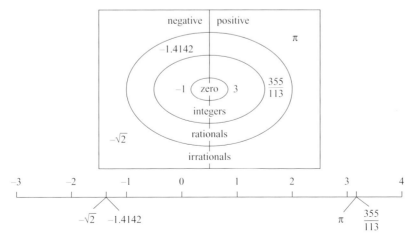

[Note: impossible to show π and $\dfrac{355}{113}$ or $-\sqrt{2}$ and -1.4142 separately on this scale.]

Activity (Page 13)

(i) counting number

(ii) rational number

(iii) irrational number

(iv) negative integer

(v) integers

(vi) no real solution

Activity (Page 14)

$(3 - 7j)^2 - 6(3 - 7j) + 58 = 9 - 42j + 49j^2 - 18 + 42j + 58$

$= 9 - 42j - 49 - 18 + 42j + 58 = 0$

Exercise 2A (Page 15)

1 $14 + 10j$

2 $5 + 2j$

3 $-3 + 4j$

4 $-1 + j$

5 21

6 $12 + 21j$

7 $\frac{5}{6} + \frac{10}{3}j$

8 $\frac{11}{3} + \frac{23}{3}j$

9 $40 + 42j$

10 100

11 $43 + 76j$

12 $-9 + 46j$

Activity (Page 16)

$(p + qj)(x + yj) = 1 \Rightarrow px - qy + (py + qx)j = 1$

$\Rightarrow px - qy = 1$ and $py + qx = 0 \Rightarrow p = \dfrac{x}{x^2 + y^2}$, $q = \dfrac{-y}{x^2 + y^2}$

Exercise 2B (Page 17)

1 $\frac{3}{10} - \frac{1}{10}j$

2 $\frac{6}{37} + \frac{1}{37}j$

3 $-\frac{1}{4} + \frac{3}{4}j$

4 $\frac{4}{5} + \frac{11}{10}j$

5 $7 - 5j$

6 $-1 - \frac{3}{2}j$

7 **(i)** $z = 11 - 10j$

   (ii) $z = \frac{34}{5} + \frac{22}{5}j$, $w = \frac{44}{5} - \frac{33}{5}j$

8 $z = 8 - 6j$, $w = 6 - 5j$

9 $a^3 - 3ab^2 + (3a^2b - b^3)j$; $z = 1$ or $\dfrac{-1 \pm \sqrt{3}j}{2}$

10 **(i)** $-j$

   (ii) 1

   (iii) j

   (iv) $-j$

   (v) -1

   $j^n = 1, j, -1, -j$ when $n = 4k, 4k + 1, 4k + 2, 4k + 3$ respectively

11 **(i)** **(a)** 0

      (b) -1

   (ii) $q - p + 1$ is a multiple of 4

12 **(i)** $ac - bd + (ad + bc)j$

13 **(i)** $\pm 4j$

   (ii) $-2 \pm 4j$

   (iii) $\dfrac{2 \pm 5j}{3}$

   (iv) $2j, 3j$

14 **(ii)** **(a)** $z^2 - 14z + 65 = 0$

      (b) $9z^2 + 25 = 0$

      (c) $z^2 + 4z + 12 = 0$

      (d) $z^2 - (5 + 3j)z + 4 + 7j = 0$

15 No

16 **(i)** $a = 5, b = 2$

   (ii) $a = 3, b = -7$

   (iii) $a = 1.25, b = -0.75$

   (iv) $a = b = \frac{1}{\sqrt{2}}$

17 $a = -7, b = 11$; other solution is $z = 5 - 2j$

18 **(i)** $(z + 2j)(z - 2j)$

   (ii) $(z + 3 + 2j)(z + 3 - 2j)$

   (iii) $(z + \frac{1}{2} + \frac{\sqrt{3}}{2}j)(z + \frac{1}{2} - \frac{\sqrt{3}}{2}j)$

   (iv) $(z + 1)(z - \frac{1}{2} + \frac{\sqrt{3}}{2}j)(z - \frac{1}{2} - \frac{\sqrt{3}}{2}j)$

19 **(i)** **(a)** $2j$

      (b) -4

      (c) $(-4)^k$

Activity (Page 20)

1 Half turn about O

2 Reflection in the real axis

Exercise 2C (Page 20)

1–6

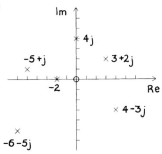

7

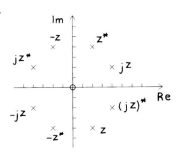

8 Points **(i)** $10 + 5j$

(ii) $1 + 2j$

(iii) $11 + 7j$

(iv) $9 + 3j$

(v) $-9 - 3j$

(vi) $25j$

(vii) $4 - 3j$

(viii) $\frac{4}{25} + \frac{3}{25}j$

9

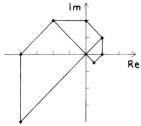

The half-squares formed are enlarged by $\sqrt{2}$, and rotated through $\frac{\pi}{4}$ each time.

10 Half a turn about O followed by reflection in the x axis is the same as reflection in the x axis followed by half a turn about O.

Activity (Page 22)

1 The diagram is as figure 2.7 but with the arrow reversed.

2

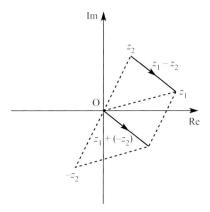

Exercise 2D (Page 22)

1 (i)

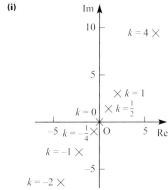

(iii) on a straight line through O

2 (i)

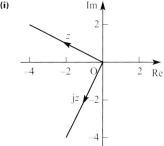

(iii) vector jz = vector z turned through $+\frac{\pi}{2}$

(iv) turning through $\frac{\pi}{2}$ twice = turning through π, which corresponds to multiplying by -1.

3

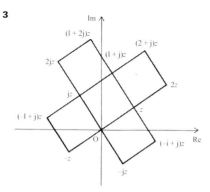

5 $\overrightarrow{AB} = b - a$, $\overrightarrow{DC} = c - d$

6 $2j, -6 + 6j, 4 - 8j$

7 (i) $2 + 3j, 4 - 2j$
  (ii) $4 + 7j, -j$

8 (i) $1, 9 - 4j$
  (ii) $-1 + 6j, -5 - 2j$ or $15 - 2j, 11 - 10j$

Exercise 2E (Page 25)

1

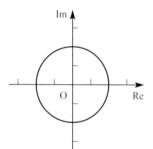

2

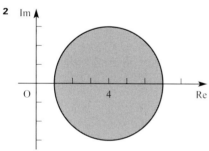

3

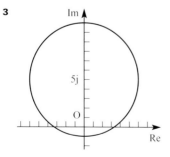

4

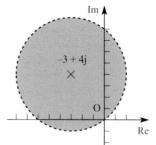

5

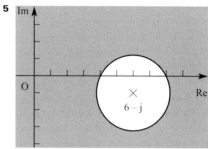

6

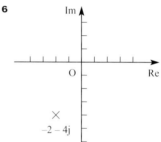

7

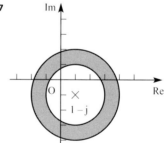

8

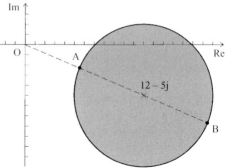

$|z|$ is least at A and greatest at B.

9 7, 13

10 Not possible

11
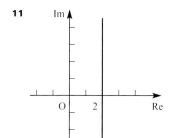

12
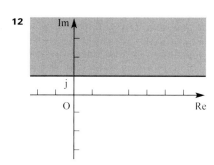

13
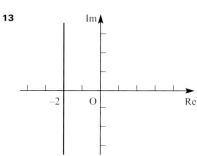

14
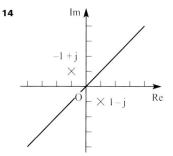

15
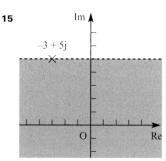

16
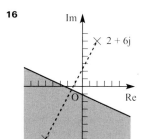

17
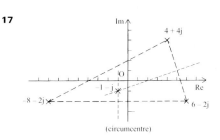

(circumcentre)

18
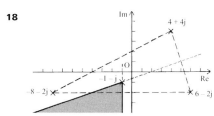

Activity (Page 26)

Properties **1**, **2**, **3** and **6** follow immediately on substituting $z_1 = x_1 + y_1 j$, $z_2 = x_2 + y_2 j$.

$$\textbf{5} \quad \left(\frac{z_1}{z_2}\right)^\star = \left(\frac{x_1 x_2 + y_1 y_2 + (y_1 x_2 - x_1 y_2)j}{x_2^2 + y_2^2}\right)^\star$$

$$= \frac{x_1 x_2 + y_1 y_2 - (y_1 x_2 - x_1 y_2)j}{x_2^2 + y_2^2} = \frac{(x_1 - y_1 j)(x_2 + y_2 j)}{(x_2 - y_2 j)(x_2 + y_2 j)} = \frac{z_1^\star}{z_2^\star}$$

Activity (Page 26)

At each stage multiply both sides by $z^\star$ and use property **4**:

$(z^k)^\star = (z^\star)^k \Rightarrow (z^k)^\star z^\star = (z^\star)^k z^\star = (z^\star)^{k+1}$,
and $(z^k)^\star z^\star = (z^k z)^\star = (z^{k+1})^\star$

The result follows. (This is done more formally on page 64.)

Activity (Page 26)

7 $|z_1 z_2|^2 = z_1 z_2 (z_1 z_2)^\star = z_1 z_2 z_1^\star z_2^\star = z_1 z_1^\star z_2 z_2^\star$
$= |z_1|^2 |z_2|^2$. The result follows since $|z| \geqslant 0$.

The proof for property **8** is similar.

Exercise 2F (Page 27)

1 (i) 2

   (ii) −4

   (iii) 8 + j

   (iv) 0

   (v) −46 − 9j

   (vi) −46 − 9j

   (vii) 52j

2 $\dfrac{2x}{x^2 + y^2}$

4 (ii) $-\dfrac{1}{2}j$

5 (i) $z^\star w$

6 (i) −115 + 236j, −115 − 236j

   (ii) $41^3 = 115^2 + 236^2$

7 $0, 2, -1 \pm \sqrt{3}j$

9 Equality occurs when vectors z_1, z_2 have the same direction and sense, or when one or both are zero.

10 (i) 4 − 3j

    (ii) −4 + 3j

Exercise 2G (Page 29)

1 2 − j, − 3

2 7, 4 ± 2j

3 $p = 4$, $q = -10$; other roots 1 + j, −6

4 3 ± 2j, 2 ± j

5 ±3j, $4 \pm \sqrt{5}$

6 (i) −2j, −2 − 2j, −4

   (ii) $p = -4$, $q = 2$

   (iii) two of 1 − j, 1 + j, −1, −4

7 (i) $(z - 5j)(z + 5j)(z + 3 - j)(z + 3 + j)$

   (ii) $U(z) = z^2 + 3z - 5$, $V(z) = -6z - 15$. (Using the factors in a different order can give different $U(z)$ and $V(z)$.)

Activity (Page 30)

(i) $\dfrac{\pi}{2}$

(ii) $\dfrac{\pi}{6}$

(iii) $-\dfrac{3\pi}{4}$

(iv) $-\dfrac{2\pi}{3}$

Activity (Page 31)

$\dfrac{\pi}{4}, -\dfrac{\pi}{4}, \dfrac{3\pi}{4}, -\dfrac{3\pi}{4}$

Exercise 2H (Page 32)

1 1, 0

2 2, π

3 $3, \dfrac{\pi}{2}$

4 $4, -\dfrac{\pi}{2}$

5 $\sqrt{2} \approx 1.414, \dfrac{\pi}{4}$

6 $\sqrt{50} \approx 7.071, -\dfrac{3\pi}{4}$

7 $2, -\dfrac{\pi}{3}$

8 $12, \dfrac{\pi}{6}$

9 $6, \dfrac{3\pi}{4}$

10 $8, \dfrac{\pi}{5}$

11 0.25, 2.3

12 $3, \pi - 3 \approx 0.142$

13 5, −0.927

14 13, 2.747

15 8.062, 1.052

16 109.604, −2.128

17 (i) $\alpha - \pi$

    (ii) $-\alpha$

    (iii) $\pi - \alpha$

    (iv) $\dfrac{\pi}{2} - \alpha$

    (v) $\dfrac{\pi}{2} + \alpha$

18 $\cos(-\alpha) + j\sin(-\alpha)$

19 $3\left[\cos\left(\dfrac{\pi}{2} - \alpha\right) + j\sin\left(\dfrac{\pi}{2} - \alpha\right)\right]$

20 $\cos\left(\dfrac{\pi}{2} + \alpha\right) + j\sin\left(\dfrac{\pi}{2} + \alpha\right)$

21 $10[\cos(-\alpha) + j\sin(-\alpha)]$

22 $\sec\alpha(\cos\alpha + j\sin\alpha)$

23 (i) Rhombus; $|z| = 2\cos\dfrac{\theta}{2}$, $\arg z = \dfrac{\theta}{2}$

    (iii) $2\sin\dfrac{\theta}{2}\left[\cos\left(\dfrac{\theta}{2} - \dfrac{\pi}{2}\right) + j\sin\left(\dfrac{\theta}{2} - \dfrac{\pi}{2}\right)\right]$

24 (i) $-3 - 4j$, $11 - 2j$

   (ii) $-1 - 2j$, -5

   (iii) $\sqrt{5} \approx 2.236$, ± 2.034 or 5, π

   (iv) L is the circle centre $-\frac{5}{2}$, radius $\frac{5}{2}$

Exercise 2I (Page 34)

1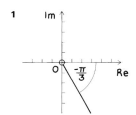

2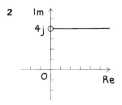

3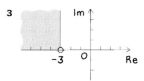

4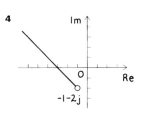

5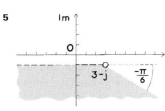

6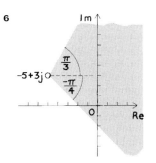

7 $\dfrac{\pi}{3}$, $\dfrac{2\pi}{3}$

8 $k \leqslant |z + 2k| \leqslant 3k$, $-\dfrac{\pi}{6} \leqslant \arg(z + 2k) \leqslant \dfrac{\pi}{6}$

9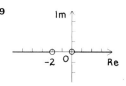

10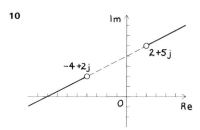

11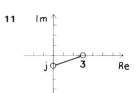

12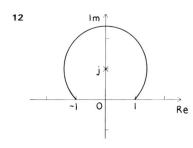

Activity (Page 35)

(i) Rotation of vector z through $+\dfrac{\pi}{2}$

(ii) Half turn of vector z

    ($= 2$ successive $\dfrac{\pi}{2}$ rotations: $-1 = j \times j$)

Exercise 2J (Page 36)

1 $6\left(\cos\dfrac{7\pi}{12} + j\sin\dfrac{7\pi}{12}\right)$

2 $\dfrac{3}{2}\left(\cos\dfrac{\pi}{12} + j\sin\dfrac{\pi}{12}\right)$

3 $\dfrac{2}{3}\left[\cos\left(-\dfrac{\pi}{12}\right) + j\sin\left(-\dfrac{\pi}{12}\right)\right]$

4 $\dfrac{1}{2}\left[\cos\left(-\dfrac{\pi}{4}\right) + j\sin\left(-\dfrac{\pi}{4}\right)\right]$

5 $9\left(\cos\dfrac{2\pi}{3} + j\sin\dfrac{2\pi}{3}\right)$

6 $32\left[\cos\left(-\dfrac{3\pi}{4}\right) + j\sin\left(-\dfrac{3\pi}{4}\right)\right]$

7 $432(\cos 0 + j\sin 0)$

8 $10\left(\cos\frac{3\pi}{4} + j\sin\frac{7\pi}{12}\right)$

9 $3\sqrt{2}\left(\cos\frac{7\pi}{12} + j\sin\frac{7\pi}{12}\right)$

10 Exceptions

(i) if $z = 0$ then $\frac{1}{z}$ does not exist

(iii) if z is real and negative then $\arg\left(\frac{1}{z}\right) = \arg z$

11 (i) Enlarge from $O \times 3$

(ii) Enlarge from $O \times 2$ and rotate $+\frac{\pi}{2}$

(iii) Complete the parallelogram $3z$, 0, $2jz$

(iv) Reflect in the real axis

(v) Find where the circle with centre O through z meets the positive real axis

(vi) Complete the similar triangles 0, 1, z and 0 , z, z^2

12 (a) All move in straight lines

(i) from $-3j$ to $3j$

(ii) from 2 to -2

(iii) from $-2 + 3j$ to $2 - 3j$

(iv) from j to $-j$

(v) from 1 to 0 then back to 1

(vi) from -1 to 0 then back to -1

(b) all except (v) move round circles

(i) once anticlockwise round $|z| = 3$, starting at 3

(ii) once anticlockwise round $|z| = 2$, starting at $2j$

(iii) once anticlockwise round $|z| = \sqrt{13}$, starting at $3 + 2j$

(iv) once clockwise round $|z| = 1$, starting at 1

(v) stationary at 1

(vi) twice anticlockwise round $|z| = 1$, starting at 1

14 $\dfrac{\sqrt{3} + 1}{2\sqrt{2}}$

15 (ii) $\dfrac{\pi}{4}$, $\dfrac{5\pi}{6}$

(iii) 8, $-\dfrac{11\pi}{12}$

(iv) perpendicular bisector of line from α to β.

(v) $\dfrac{13\pi}{24}$

16 (i) Points of knife have moduli < 1, which decrease on squaring; angle subtended by knife at the origin is doubled

(ii) points of forearm have argument $\dfrac{\pi}{2}$ (vertical from O) which doubles to become π (horizontal from O) on squaring

(iii) angles subtended by head and boots at O both double, but boots are further from O than head, so grow more

(iv) knife tip has argument $\dfrac{3\pi}{4}$, stomach has argument $-\dfrac{\pi}{4}$; both give argument $-\dfrac{\pi}{2}$ on doubling.

Chapter 3

? (Page 44)

No

Exercise 3A (Page 45)

1 (i) $\begin{pmatrix} -23 \\ 13 \\ 2 \end{pmatrix}$

(ii) $\begin{pmatrix} 37 \\ 41 \\ 19 \end{pmatrix}$

(iii) $\begin{pmatrix} -8 \\ 34 \\ 27 \end{pmatrix}$

(iv) $21\mathbf{i} - 29\mathbf{j} + 9\mathbf{k}$

3 (i) $\begin{pmatrix} 5 \\ 19 \\ -2 \end{pmatrix}$

(ii) $\begin{pmatrix} 14 \\ -62 \\ -9 \end{pmatrix}$

(iii) $\begin{pmatrix} -3 \\ -2 \\ 3 \end{pmatrix}$

(iv) $\begin{pmatrix} -18 \\ 57 \\ 47 \end{pmatrix}$

4 $\begin{pmatrix} \dfrac{19}{\sqrt{635}} \\ \dfrac{15}{\sqrt{635}} \\ \dfrac{-7}{\sqrt{635}} \end{pmatrix}$

5 (i) $5x + 4y - 8z = 5$

(ii) $24x + y - 29z = 1$

(iii) $19x + 40y + 3z = 188$

(iv) $30x - 29y - 24z = 86$

6 (i) $\begin{pmatrix} -1 \\ -12 \\ -31 \end{pmatrix}$; $\sqrt{1106}$, $\sqrt{\dfrac{1106}{1155}}$

(ii) $\dfrac{7}{\sqrt{1155}}$

(iv) Using $\sin\theta$ does not indicate whether θ is acute or obtuse.

7 The plane containing $\mathbf{a}$ and $\mathbf{b}$ also contains $\mathbf{c}$.

8 $\mathbf{a} \times \mathbf{b}$ is perpendicular to $\mathbf{a}$.

9 $k = -5$

? (Page 51)

π_3 is parallel to π_1 and π_2 (the common line is at infinity).

Exercise 3B (Page 52)

1 (i) $\dfrac{x-3}{15} = \dfrac{y-1}{27} = \dfrac{z}{7}$

(ii) $x = y + 3 = \dfrac{z-5}{-4}$

(iii) $\dfrac{x}{16} = \dfrac{y+1}{15} = \dfrac{z+1}{13}$

(iv) $\dfrac{x-2}{11} = \dfrac{y}{4} = \dfrac{z-4}{21}$

2 (i) $56.5°$

(ii) $80.0°$

(iii) $24.9°$

(iv) $63.5°$

3 (i) $x + 2 = y - 3 = -(z-5)$

(ii) $\dfrac{x-4}{3} = \dfrac{y+3}{2} = \dfrac{z-2}{-6}$

4 $41x - 19y + 26z = 33$

5 $x + 3y - z + 8 = 0$

6 $\dfrac{x-4}{21} = \dfrac{y+2}{4} = \dfrac{z+7}{11}$

7 $60x + 11y + 100z = 900$; $60x - 11y - 100z + 300 = 0$;
$\mathbf{r} = \begin{pmatrix} 5 \\ 0 \\ 6 \end{pmatrix} + t \begin{pmatrix} 0 \\ 100 \\ -11 \end{pmatrix}$; $6.3°$

8 (i) $x + 3z + 800 = 0$

(ii) Normal is $18.4°$ approx to horizontal

(iii) $14x - 15y + 3450z - 15\,950 = 0$

(iv) $x = 15\lambda$, $y = -1136\lambda - 62\,396.7$, $z = -5\lambda - 266.7$

(v) 62 km (assuming seam is sufficiently extensive)

9 (i) $(2, -5, 3)$

(ii) $(-1, -3, 4)$

(iii) $(5, -2, 1)$

10 $\pi_4 = \pi_5$ because π_1, π_2, π_3 have a common line.

11 (i) $22\mathbf{i} - 44\mathbf{j} + 55\mathbf{k}$

(ii) $\dfrac{x-2}{2} = \dfrac{y+2}{-4} = \dfrac{z}{5}$

(iii) $a = 3$, $d = -2$

Exercise 3C (Page 56)

1 (i) $(3, 2, -13)$

(ii) $(1, 2, 7)$

(iii) Do not meet

(iv) $(4, -7, 11)$

(v) Do not meet

2 No

3 $(-2, -6, -1)$; 30 units

4 $6, 9, \sqrt{77}$

5 (i) $7\mathbf{i} - 7\mathbf{j} + 14\mathbf{k}$

(ii) $(11, 6, -2)$

(iii) $x - y + 2z - 1 = 0$

(iv) $11x - 5y - 8z - 107 = 0$

6 (i) $-\mathbf{i} + 6\mathbf{j} - 18\mathbf{k}$

(ii) $6, (-17, 22, 14)$

(iii) $-x + 6y - 18z + 103 = 0$

(iv) 5

8 (ii) $(3p - 1, -4p - 4, 7p + 5)$, $(12, 2q, -3q + 2)$

(iii) $\mathbf{r} = \begin{pmatrix} 8 \\ 6 \\ -8 \end{pmatrix} + t \begin{pmatrix} 2 \\ 1 \\ -1 \end{pmatrix}$

(iv) $(-4, 0, -2)$, $(12, 8, -10)$

9 (iii) $(1, -5, 1)$, $(-1, -1, 5)$, $(-1, 5, -1)$, $(1, 1, -5)$, $(-3, -3, -3)$, $(-5, 1, 1)$

10 (ii) $\begin{pmatrix} 1 \\ 2 \\ -2 \end{pmatrix}, \begin{pmatrix} 22 \\ -1 \\ 10 \end{pmatrix}$

(iii) $22x - y + 10z = 123$

(iv) $(-1, -15, 13)$

(v) $\dfrac{x+1}{1} = \dfrac{y+15}{2} = \dfrac{z-13}{-2}$

(vi) $(8, 3, -5)$; 27 units

11 41.9 m; $(8, 42, -11)$, $(41, 21, 4)$

Chapter 4

Activity (Page 60)

1 See text which follows.

2 $1, 2, 4, 8$; predict $16, 32$; actually $16, 31$

Activity (Page 62)

1 Left-hand side is always an integer, right-hand side is never an integer.

2 e.g. $2 + 4 + 6 + \ldots + 2n = 2n$

Exercise 4A (Page 64)

1 n^2

2 $\dfrac{n(3n + 5)}{2}$

3 $\dfrac{n}{n + 1}$

4 $\dfrac{n}{2n + 1}$

5 $(n + 1)! - 1$

6 $\dfrac{n+1}{2n}(n \geq 2)$

7 $\dfrac{1}{n}$

8 $3^n - 1$

12 $(ac + bd)^2 + (ad - bc)^2$ or $(ac - bd)^2 + (ad + bc)^2$

13 **(ii)** requires $n \geq 2$; there is no argument to get from $n = 1$ to $n = 2$

Exercise 4B (Page 67)

1 Always divisible by 7

4 **(i)** $u_n = 2$

    (ii) $u_n = 4^{n-1} + 2$

5 **(i)** 13, 35

8 Since $(3 - \sqrt{5})^n < 0.5$ for $n > 1$, u_n is the integer nearest to $(3 + \sqrt{5})^n$. Divisibility by 2^n comes from the recurrence relation by induction.

9 7

10 $n = 1$ or $n \geq 10$

11 **(iv)** Equality if and only if $x_1 = x_2 = \ldots = x_n$

Activity (Page 70)

1 **(i)** True when $n = 1$ since $u_1 = v_0 - v_1$ by definition.
    (ii) True when $n = k$

$$\Rightarrow \sum_{r=1}^{k} u_r = v_0 - v_k$$

$$\Rightarrow \sum_{r=1}^{k+1} u_r = v_0 - v_k + u_{k+1} = v_0 - v_k + v_k - v_{k+1}$$
$$= v_0 - v_{k+1}$$
$$\Rightarrow \text{true when } n = k + 1.$$

From **(i)** and **(ii)** by induction, statement is true for all $n \geq 1$.

2 $v_r = -(2r + 1)^3$

3 $\frac{1}{3}n(n + 1)(n + 2)$

Exercise 4C (Page 74)

1 n^2

2 $n(n + 1)^2$

3 $\frac{1}{12}n(n + 1)(n + 2)(3n + 1)$

4 n^4

5 $\frac{9}{2}n^2(3n^2 - 1)$

6 7

10 **(ii)** **(a)** $\dfrac{3}{r+1} - \dfrac{3}{r+3}$

    (b) $3\left(\dfrac{5}{6} - \dfrac{1}{n+2} - \dfrac{1}{n+3}\right)\left(= \dfrac{n(5n + 13)}{2(n+2)(n+3)}\right)$

11 $\dfrac{n(3n + 5)}{4(n+1)(n+2)}$

12 $\dfrac{n(n + 1)}{6(n+3)(n+4)}$

13 $\dfrac{n(n + 3)}{4(n+1)(n+2)}$

14 $\dfrac{n(n + 2)}{(n+1)^2}$

16 **(i)** $\dfrac{1}{4}n(n + 1)(n + 2)(n + 3)$

    (ii) $\dfrac{1}{k+2}n(n + 1)(n + 2)\ldots(n + k + 1)$

18 $\dfrac{1}{2} - \dfrac{1}{(n+1)2^{n+1}}$

19 $T = \dfrac{1 - (n+1)x^n + nx^{n+1}}{(1 - x)^2}$

20 $1 - \dfrac{x^n}{(x+1)(x+2)\ldots(x+n)}$

Chapter 5

❓ (Page 78)

Shear followed by rotation.

Activity (Page 80)

(i) $\begin{pmatrix} 0 & -1 \\ 1 & 0 \end{pmatrix}$

(ii) $\begin{pmatrix} 0 & 1 \\ 1 & 0 \end{pmatrix}$

(iii) $\begin{pmatrix} 2 & 0 \\ 0 & 2 \end{pmatrix}$

Activity (Page 81)

(ii) $\begin{pmatrix} 1 & 2 \\ 0 & 1 \end{pmatrix}$

Activity (Page 82)

1 The origin moves.

2 $x' = 2x - y, \ y' = x, \begin{pmatrix} 2 & -1 \\ 1 & 0 \end{pmatrix}$

Activity (Page 83)

$(\cos2\theta, \sin2\theta), (\sin2\theta, -\cos2\theta)$

❓ (Page 86)

Three co-ordinates are needed to fix the position of a point in three-dimensional space. Points for which one co-ordinate is fixed, or is a linear expression of the other two co-ordinates, form a two-dimensional space embedded in the three-dimensional space. Similarly for one-dimensional spaces embedded in two- or three-dimensional spaces.

Exercise 5A (Page 87)

1 (i) $\begin{pmatrix} 3 & 0 \\ 0 & 3 \end{pmatrix}$ (ii) $\begin{pmatrix} 1 & 0 \\ 0 & -1 \end{pmatrix}$

(iii) $\begin{pmatrix} 0 & -1 \\ -1 & 0 \end{pmatrix}$ (iv) $\begin{pmatrix} 0 & 1 \\ -1 & 0 \end{pmatrix}$

(v) $\begin{pmatrix} \frac{1}{2} & 0 \\ 0 & \frac{1}{2} \end{pmatrix}$

2 (i)   Reflection in the x axis.
   (ii)   Reflection in $y = x$.
   (iii)   Two way stretch, ×2 parallel to x axis, ×3 parallel to y axis.
   (iv)   Enlargement, ×3, centre O.
   (v)   Rotation 45° anticlockwise about O.
   (vi)   Rotation through arccos 0.6 anticlockwise about O.
   (vii)   Two way stretch, ×2 parallel to x axis, ×$\frac{1}{2}$ parallel to y axis.
   (viii) Shear, with fixed line $x + y = 0$, with e.g. $(0, -1)$ moving to $(1, 0)$.
   (ix)   Projection (perpendicularly) on to the x axis.

3 $(8, 10), (2, 3), (16, 21)$

4 $(x, x); \begin{pmatrix} 1 & 0 \\ 1 & 0 \end{pmatrix}$

5 Shear with fixed line $x + y = 0$, with e.g. $(1, 0)$ moving to $(0, 1)$

6 (iii) Shear with fixed line $x - 2y = 0$, with e.g. $(1, 0)$ moving to $(3, 1)$

7 (i) $\begin{pmatrix} 3 & 0 & 0 \\ 0 & 3 & 0 \\ 0 & 0 & 3 \end{pmatrix}$

(ii) $\begin{pmatrix} -1 & 0 & 0 \\ 0 & -1 & 0 \\ 0 & 0 & 1 \end{pmatrix}$

(iii) $\begin{pmatrix} 1 & 0 & 0 \\ 0 & 0 & 1 \\ 0 & 1 & 0 \end{pmatrix}$

8 (i)   Rotation of three-dimensional space 180° about the x axis.
   (ii)   Reflection of three-dimensional space in the plane $x = y$.
   (iii)   Shear with fixed plane $z = 0$, with e.g. $(0, 0, 1)$ moving to $(3, 0, 1)$.
   (iv)   Forming the two-dimensional 'end elevation' of a three-dimensional object, using a scale of 1 : 100.

Activity (Page 89)

Addition of elelments in each position is (i) commutative, (ii) associative.

Activity (Page 92)

(i) $\begin{pmatrix} 14 & 2 \\ -14 & 11 \end{pmatrix}$ (ii) $\begin{pmatrix} 60 & -40 \\ -34 & 53 \end{pmatrix}$

(iii) $\begin{pmatrix} 14 & -18 \\ 8 & -1 \end{pmatrix}$ (iv) = (ii)

❓ (Page 93)

Pre- and post-multiplying would give matrices of different orders.

Activity (Page 94)

$wa + yb = 1, wc + yd = 0; xa + zb = 0, xc + zd = 1$

Exercise 5B (Page 95)

1 (i) $\begin{pmatrix} 0 & 8 \\ 4 & 9 \end{pmatrix}$

(ii) $\begin{pmatrix} 6 & 9 & 12 \\ 15 & 21 & 3 \end{pmatrix}$

(iii) Not possible

(iv) Not possible

(v) $\begin{pmatrix} -1 & -3 \\ 4 & 2 \\ 0 & -7 \end{pmatrix}$

(vi) $\begin{pmatrix} -7 & 26 \\ 2 & 34 \end{pmatrix}$

(vii) Not possible

(viii) $\begin{pmatrix} 29 & 40 & -5 \\ 29 & 41 & 13 \end{pmatrix}$

(ix) $\begin{pmatrix} 31 & 0 \\ 65 & 18 \end{pmatrix}$

(x) $\begin{pmatrix} 26 & 37 & 16 \\ 14 & 21 & 28 \\ -8 & -11 & 2 \end{pmatrix}$

(xi) Not possible

(xii) Not possible

(xiii) $\begin{pmatrix} 55 & 89 & 3 \\ 4 & 19 & 10 \\ 23 & 54 & 41 \end{pmatrix}$

(xiv) $\begin{pmatrix} 26 & 32 \\ 5 & -5 \\ 13 & 21 \end{pmatrix}$

(xv) $\begin{pmatrix} 28 & -18 \\ 26 & 2 \\ 16 & 25 \end{pmatrix}$

3 $(\mathbf{AC})\mathbf{F} = \mathbf{A}(\mathbf{CF}) = \begin{pmatrix} 52 & 225 & 49 \\ 128 & 420 & -24 \end{pmatrix}$

4 (i) $\begin{pmatrix} 0.4 & -0.1 \\ -0.2 & 0.3 \end{pmatrix}$

(ii) $\begin{pmatrix} -\frac{5}{29} & \frac{7}{29} \\ \frac{2}{29} & \frac{3}{29} \end{pmatrix}$

(iii) $\begin{pmatrix} -7 & 26 \\ 2 & 34 \end{pmatrix}$

(iv) $\begin{pmatrix} -\frac{17}{145} & \frac{13}{145} \\ \frac{1}{145} & \frac{7}{290} \end{pmatrix}$

$\mathbf{B}^{-1}\mathbf{A}^{-1}$

5 (i) $\begin{pmatrix} \frac{5}{2} & -\frac{3}{2} \\ -3 & 2 \end{pmatrix}$

(ii) $\begin{pmatrix} \frac{1}{12} & -\frac{1}{8} \\ -\frac{1}{6} & -\frac{1}{4} \end{pmatrix}$

(iii) $\begin{pmatrix} 1 & -2 \\ -\frac{2}{3} & \frac{5}{3} \end{pmatrix}$

(iv) $\begin{pmatrix} 12 & -\frac{9}{2} \\ -4 & 2 \end{pmatrix}$

(v) $\dfrac{1}{eh-fg}\begin{pmatrix} h & -f \\ -g & e \end{pmatrix}$ provided $eh \neq fg$

6 $k = 2$ or 3

7 (ii) Reflection in $y = 2x$

8 (i) $(3, 1), (1, 1), (-6, -2)$

(ii) $2 : 1; 2$

9 (iii) $\begin{pmatrix} 5 & 0 \\ 0 & 5 \end{pmatrix}$

(iv) Englargement, $\times 5$, centre O

10 (i) $\begin{pmatrix} 2 & -\frac{3}{2} \\ -3 & \frac{5}{2} \end{pmatrix}$

(ii) $\begin{pmatrix} \frac{2}{5} & -\frac{3}{5} \\ -\frac{1}{5} & \frac{4}{5} \end{pmatrix}$

(iii) $\begin{pmatrix} 1.1 & -2.4 \\ -1.7 & 3.8 \end{pmatrix}$

(iv) $\begin{pmatrix} 2.6 & -2.1 \\ -2.8 & 2.3 \end{pmatrix}$

(v) $\begin{pmatrix} 1.1 & -2.4 \\ -1.7 & 3.8 \end{pmatrix}$

(vi) $\begin{pmatrix} 2.6 & -2.1 \\ -2.8 & 2.3 \end{pmatrix}$

$(\mathbf{BA})^{-1} = \mathbf{A}^{-1}\mathbf{B}^{-1}; (\mathbf{AB})^{-1} = \mathbf{B}^{-1}\mathbf{A}^{-1}$

11 $\mathbf{M}^2 = (a + d)\mathbf{M}, \mathbf{M}^n = (a + d)^{n-1}\mathbf{M}$

12 (i) $\mathbf{D} = (1 \quad 1)$

(ii) $\mathbf{N} = \begin{pmatrix} 1 \\ 1 \\ 1 \\ 1 \\ 1 \end{pmatrix}$

(iii) $(27 \quad 19)\mathbf{SN}$

13 $\mathbf{M} = \begin{pmatrix} 1 & 1 & 2 & 0 \\ 1 & 0 & 1 & 0 \\ 1 & 1 & 0 & 2 \\ 0 & 0 & 1 & 0 \end{pmatrix}$ $\mathbf{M}^2 = \begin{pmatrix} 4 & 3 & 3 & 4 \\ 2 & 2 & 2 & 2 \\ 2 & 1 & 5 & 0 \\ 1 & 1 & 0 & 2 \end{pmatrix}$

$\mathbf{M}^2$ gives the number of 'two-stage' routes between the resorts. $\mathbf{M}^3$ gives the number of 'three-stage' routes between the resorts.

14 (ii) $\begin{pmatrix} 1 & 0 & 0 \\ 0 & 0 & 1 \\ 0 & 1 & 0 \end{pmatrix}$

(iii) $\begin{pmatrix} 0 & 1 & 0 \\ 0 & 0 & 1 \\ 1 & 0 & 0 \end{pmatrix}$

(iv) $\begin{pmatrix} 0 & 0 & 1 \\ 1 & 0 & 0 \\ 0 & 1 & 0 \end{pmatrix}, \begin{pmatrix} c \\ a \\ b \end{pmatrix}$

(v) $\begin{pmatrix} 1 & 0 & 0 \\ 0 & 1 & 0 \\ 0 & 0 & 1 \end{pmatrix}$; After 6 stages the strands will be in their original order.

15 (i) $\begin{pmatrix} 1 & -R_1 \\ 0 & 1 \end{pmatrix}$

(ii) $\begin{pmatrix} 1 & 0 \\ -\frac{1}{R_2} & 1 \end{pmatrix}$

(iii) $\mathbf{BA} = \begin{pmatrix} 1 & -R_1 \\ -\frac{1}{R_2} & 1 + \frac{R_1}{R_2} \end{pmatrix}$

(iv) No

? (Page 101)

No difference, provided that the matrices in **(ii)** are compatible for multiplication.

Activity (Page 101)

$(\mathbf{AB})(\mathbf{B}^{-1}\mathbf{A}^{-1}) = \mathbf{A}(\mathbf{BB}^{-1})\mathbf{A}^{-1} = \mathbf{AIA}^{-1} = \mathbf{AA}^{-1} = \mathbf{I}$

Exercise 5C (Page 101)

1 $X = \begin{pmatrix} 1 & 0 \\ 0 & -1 \end{pmatrix}; J = \begin{pmatrix} 0 & 1 \\ -1 & 0 \end{pmatrix}$

  (i) $JX = \begin{pmatrix} 0 & -1 \\ -1 & 0 \end{pmatrix}$; reflection in $y = -x$

  (ii) $XJ = \begin{pmatrix} 0 & 1 \\ 1 & 0 \end{pmatrix}$; reflection in $y = x$

2 $RS = \begin{pmatrix} 2 & -1 \\ 1 & 3 \end{pmatrix}\begin{pmatrix} 3 & 0 \\ -2 & 4 \end{pmatrix} = \begin{pmatrix} 8 & -4 \\ -3 & 12 \end{pmatrix}$

3 $M = \begin{pmatrix} \cos2\theta & \sin2\theta \\ \sin2\theta & -\cos2\theta \end{pmatrix}$

4 $R = \begin{pmatrix} \cos\alpha & -\sin\alpha \\ \sin\alpha & \cos\alpha \end{pmatrix}$

  Inverse of rotation through α is rotation through $-\alpha$.

6 **(i)** Successive rotations about the same centre are commutative

  (ii) $R_\alpha = \begin{pmatrix} \cos\alpha & -\sin\alpha \\ \sin\alpha & \cos\alpha \end{pmatrix}$;

    $R_\beta = \begin{pmatrix} \cos\beta & -\sin\beta \\ \sin\beta & \cos\beta \end{pmatrix}$;

    $R_\alpha R_\beta = \begin{pmatrix} \cos(\alpha+\beta) & -\sin(\alpha+\beta) \\ \sin(\alpha+\beta) & \cos(\alpha+\beta) \end{pmatrix}$

  (iii) $R_{\alpha+\beta}$

7 **(i)** $R = \begin{pmatrix} \frac{\sqrt{3}}{2} & -\frac{1}{2} \\ \frac{1}{2} & \frac{\sqrt{3}}{2} \end{pmatrix}$; $M = \begin{pmatrix} -\frac{1}{2} & \frac{\sqrt{3}}{2} \\ \frac{\sqrt{3}}{2} & \frac{1}{2} \end{pmatrix}$

  (ii) $MR = \begin{pmatrix} 0 & 1 \\ 1 & 0 \end{pmatrix}$; reflection in $y = x$

  (iii) Reflection in $y = (2 + \sqrt{3})x$

8 $M = \begin{pmatrix} 2 & -\frac{1}{3} \\ 3 & 0 \end{pmatrix}$

9 **(i)** $\begin{pmatrix} \cos2\alpha & -\sin2\alpha \\ \sin2\alpha & \cos2\alpha \end{pmatrix}$

  (ii) $\begin{pmatrix} \cos2\theta & \sin2\theta \\ \sin2\theta & -\cos2\theta \end{pmatrix}$

11 **(ii)** $\begin{pmatrix} -\frac{1}{\sqrt{2}} & -\frac{1}{\sqrt{2}} \\ \frac{1}{\sqrt{2}} & -\frac{1}{\sqrt{2}} \end{pmatrix}$

  (iv) $x - 3y + 10 = 0$

12 **(ii)** **(a)** $\begin{pmatrix} 18 & -9 & 4 \\ 1 & -7 & 2 \\ -1 & -4 & 1 \end{pmatrix}$

    (b) $\begin{pmatrix} 1 & a+7 & b+7c+4 \\ 0 & 1 & c+2 \\ 0 & 0 & 1 \end{pmatrix}$

    (c) $\begin{pmatrix} 1 & -7 & 10 \\ 0 & 1 & -2 \\ 0 & 0 & 1 \end{pmatrix}$

    (d) $\begin{pmatrix} 1 & 0 & 0 \\ -3 & 1 & 0 \\ -11 & 4 & 1 \end{pmatrix}$

    (e) $\begin{pmatrix} 1 & -7 & 10 \\ -3 & 22 & -32 \\ -11 & 81 & -117 \end{pmatrix}$

13 **(i)** **(a)** $\begin{pmatrix} \frac{2}{\sqrt{5}} & \frac{1}{\sqrt{5}} \\ -\frac{1}{\sqrt{5}} & \frac{2}{\sqrt{5}} \end{pmatrix}$

    (b) $\begin{pmatrix} 5 & 0 \\ 0 & 1 \end{pmatrix}$

    (c) $\begin{pmatrix} \frac{2}{\sqrt{5}} & -\frac{1}{\sqrt{5}} \\ \frac{1}{\sqrt{5}} & \frac{2}{\sqrt{5}} \end{pmatrix}$; $S = \begin{pmatrix} \frac{21}{5} & \frac{8}{5} \\ \frac{8}{5} & \frac{9}{5} \end{pmatrix}$

  (ii) One way stretch, $\times \frac{1}{5}$ parallel to the line $y = \frac{1}{2}x$, centre O; $\begin{pmatrix} \frac{9}{25} & -\frac{8}{25} \\ -\frac{8}{25} & \frac{21}{25} \end{pmatrix}$

14 **(iii)** Enlargement $\times b$, centre O; rotation 90° anticlockwise about O; projection perpendicularly on to the x axis.

  (iv) P collapses everything on to the x axis, R rotates through $\frac{\pi}{2}$ and E enlarges. Repeating this takes everything to O.

15 **(i)** $\begin{pmatrix} -3 & -8 \\ 2 & 5 \end{pmatrix}, \begin{pmatrix} -5 & -12 \\ 3 & 7 \end{pmatrix}$

  (iv) $p = 2, q = -1$

  (v) $r = 3, s = -2$

  (vi) $A^4 = 4A - 3I$

  (vii) $A^n = nA - (n-1)I$

Activity (Page 105)

$T(\mathbf{p}) = T(\mathbf{p} + 0) = T(\mathbf{p}) + T(0) \Rightarrow T(0) = 0$. A non-zero translation moves the origin.

Exercise 5D (Page 106)

1 **(i)**, **(iv)** and **(v)** are the only linear transformations listed.

2 $\left(\frac{1}{5}p + \frac{2}{5}q, \frac{2}{5}p + \frac{4}{5}q\right)$; yes

3 See the definition on page 105. This T is not linear since, e.g., $T(5, 0) + T(-3, 0) = (5, 0) + (3, 0) = (8, 0)$ but $T(5 + (-3), 0) = (2, 0)$

6 $\mathbf{c} = \dfrac{1}{m+n}(n\mathbf{a} + m\mathbf{b})$

9 **(i)** No; translation $\begin{pmatrix} 3 \\ -5 \end{pmatrix}$

  (ii) $\begin{pmatrix} x' \\ y' \\ 1 \end{pmatrix} = \begin{pmatrix} 0 & -1 & 3 \\ 1 & 0 & -1 \\ 0 & 0 & 1 \end{pmatrix}\begin{pmatrix} x \\ y \\ 1 \end{pmatrix}$; no

10 $\begin{pmatrix} 4 & 0 & 0 & 0 & 0 \\ 0 & 3 & 0 & 0 & 0 \\ 0 & 0 & 2 & 0 & 0 \\ 0 & 0 & 0 & 1 & 0 \end{pmatrix}$

Activity (Page 108)

(i) 5

(ii) det $\mathbf{R} = -2$, det $\mathbf{S} = 0$

(iii) R changes orientation, S collapses the square to a line.

Activity (Page 108)

$\begin{pmatrix} kc \\ kd \end{pmatrix}$

❓ (Page 109)

For each such matrix (not the zero matrix) all shapes collapse to points on a line through O. For the zero matrix all shapes collapse to the origin.

Activity (Page 110)

$\begin{pmatrix} x \\ y \end{pmatrix} \rightarrow \begin{pmatrix} ax + cy \\ bx + dy \end{pmatrix}$;

$b(ax + cy) - a(bx + dy) = (bc - ad)y = 0$ since $ad - bc = 0$.

Exercise 5E (Page 110)

1 **(i)** 10, non-singular
   (ii) 0, singular
   (iii) 0, singular
   (iv) 7, non-singular

3 $\det(\mathbf{MN})$ = area scale factor of $\mathbf{N}$ followed by $\mathbf{M}$
= area scale factor of $\mathbf{M} \times$ area scale factor of $\mathbf{N}$
= det $\mathbf{M} \times$ det $\mathbf{N}$

4 $ad = 1$

5 $\left(\frac{3}{8}(3s - t), \frac{1}{8}(3s - t)\right)$; $\begin{pmatrix} \frac{9}{8} & -\frac{3}{8} \\ \frac{3}{8} & -\frac{1}{8} \end{pmatrix}$

6 **(iii)** $x + 2y = 5$

Exercise 5F (Page 116)

1 A pair of lines intersecting at $\left(6\frac{1}{2}, -\frac{1}{2}\right)$.

2 Inconsistent: distinct parallel lines in two dimensions.

3 Coincident lines with infinitely many common points: $(\lambda, 2\lambda - 4)$.

4 Inconsistent: distinct parallel lines in two dimensions.

5 Inconsistent; planes forming a prism.

6 A sheaf of planes with a common line: $(2\lambda + 1, 4\lambda + 1, -3\lambda + 5)$.

7 Three planes with unique common point: $(3, -14, 8)$.

8 Three planes with a unique common point: $(-15, 24, -1)$.

9 Three coincident planes: $(\lambda, \mu, 2\lambda + \mu - 5)$.

10 Inconsistent: planes forming a prism.

11 $k = 4$: $\left(\frac{3}{2} - 2\lambda, \lambda\right)$; $k = -4$: no solution.

12 The transformation either (a) collapses the plane to a line through O or (b) maps everything to O. When $p = q = 0$ in (a) there is a line of points which map to O, and in (b) every point maps to O. If p and q are not both zero there is *either* no solution (distinct parallel lines) *or* many solutions (coincident lines).

13 **(i)** Inconsistent: planes form a prism.

   (ii) $(\lambda - 2, \lambda, 2\lambda)$: planes form a sheaf.

14 **(i)** $\begin{pmatrix} 2 & 0 & 6 - 2k \\ 0 & 2 & k - 3 \\ 0 & 0 & 5 - k \end{pmatrix}$

   (ii) $\mathbf{Q}^{-1} = \frac{1}{2}\mathbf{P}$, $x = -7$, $y = 5$, $z = 0$
   (iii) e.g. $x = 3 - 2t$, $y = t$, $z = 5 - t$
   (iv) sheaf

15 It makes no difference whether $\mathbf{A}$ is singular or non-singular.

16 14

17 **(ii)** **(a)** No solution; prism of planes
      (b) e.g. $x = t$, $y = 3t - 4$, $z = 2t - 2$; sheaf

Activity (Page 119)

See Activity on page 105.

Activity (Page 123)

$\mathbf{d}' = \mathbf{0} \Rightarrow \mathbf{r}' = \mathbf{a}'$: the image of the line is a single point.

Exercise 5G (Page 123)

1 $(\lambda, -\lambda)$

2 $(0, 0)$

3 $(2\lambda, \lambda)$

4 $(0, 0)$

5 $y = 2x; y = -\frac{1}{2}x$

6 $y = -2x; x = 0$

7 $3y = 4x; 4y = -3x$

8 $y = 2x; y = -2x$

9 $y = x; y = x + c$

10 $x = k; y = \frac{1}{3}x + c; y = -3x$

11 $y = x; y = -x + c$

12 None

13 (i) -1 or 3
(ii) $(1, -1)$ maps to $(1, -1)$; $(1, 3)$ maps to $(13, 39)$

15 (i) 0
(ii) $m = 1, k = 0$; $m = 3, k = -2$; $y = 3x, y = x$
(degenerately)
(iii) $y = x$ maps to $(0, 0)$; $y = x + 1$ maps to $(-1, -3)$;
$y = x - 2$ maps to $(2, 6)$
(iv) All points on $y = x - 3$

16 (ii) $-1, -\frac{1}{6}$
(iii) $y = \frac{7}{2}x - 12$

17 (i) $(\lambda, 2\lambda); y = 2x$
(ii) (c) $a = -2b$

Chapter 6

❓ (Page 128)

(i) The graph has two separate branches.
(ii) Curves
(iii) They can only draw a finite number of pixels.

Activity (Page 133)

(i)

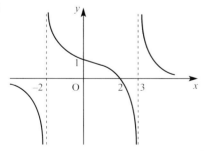

(ii)

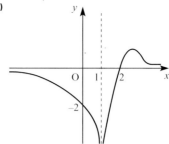

Exercise 6A (Page 136)

1

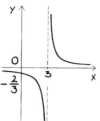

2

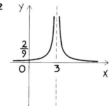

3

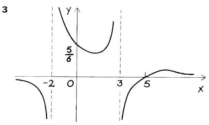

4

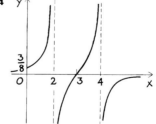

Answers

5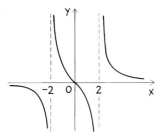

6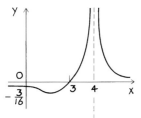

7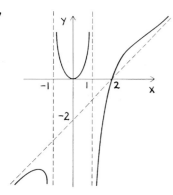

8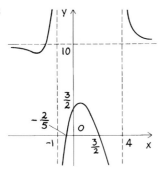

9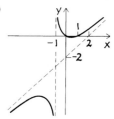

10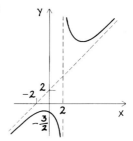

11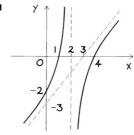

12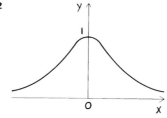

13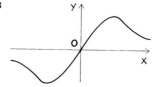

14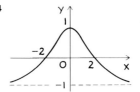

15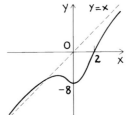

16

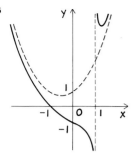

17

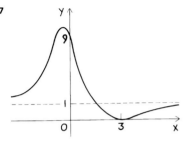

18

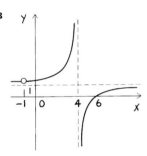

19

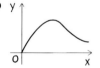

Maximum after 2 hours

20

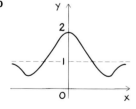

21

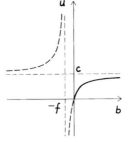

For $0 < u < c$, the gradient increases as f decreases.

22

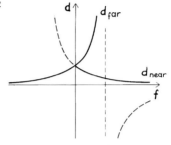

Small apertures (large f numbers) mean that a wide range of distances are in focus, suiting landscapes.

Large apertures cause small depth of field, isolating the subject from its surroundings, often suitable for portraits.

23

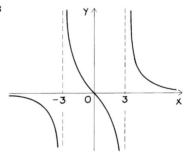

(i) $-yx^2 - x - 9y = 0$

(ii) 2

(iii) y decreases from $+\infty$ to $-\infty$ monotonically.

(iv) A turning point elsewhere would imply there are more than two values of x for a given y, which, by (ii), is impossible.

24 $y = \dfrac{x-2}{x+3}$ is equivalent to a linear equation in x, so that there is at most one value of x for every given value of y.

25 If $a = c$ and $b < a$ there is a turning point to the left of $x = b$.

Activity (Page 138)

(ii) (a) R is below Q and above $y = 1$

(b) R is at Q

(c) R is above Q and below $y = 1$

(iii) No R exists.

(iv) $y = \pm\sqrt{2 - x^2} \Leftrightarrow x^2 + y^2 = 2$, the equation of a circle.

Exercise 6B (Page 140)

1

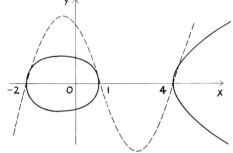

2

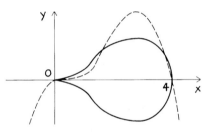

3

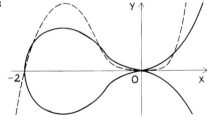

4

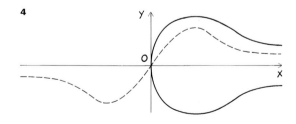

5

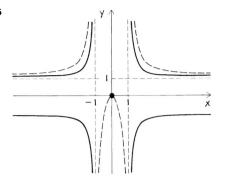

6

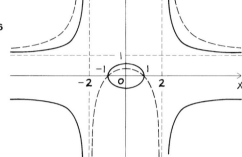

7

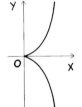

8

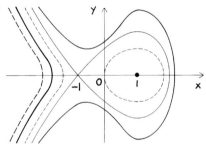

9 (i) $\left(0, \frac{2}{3}\right)$; $(2, 0)$, $(-1, 0)$

(ii) $1 - \dfrac{4}{(x - 3)^2}$; $(5, 9)$, $(1, 1)$

(iii) $y = x + 2$, oblique asymptote

(iv)

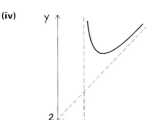

(v)

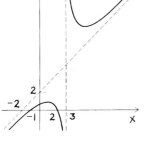

10 (i) $A = 4$, $B = 65$, asymptote $y = 4$

(ii) $\dfrac{dy}{dx} = \dfrac{260 - 65x^2}{(x^2 + 4)^2}$, $\left(-2, -12\frac{1}{4}\right)$, $\left(2, 20\frac{1}{4}\right)$

(iii)

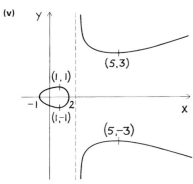

(iv)

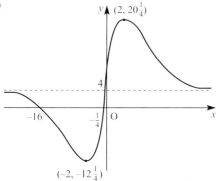

11 (i) $(1, 0)$, $(-1, 0)$, $\left(0, \dfrac{-1}{a^2}\right)$; $x = -\dfrac{a}{2}$, $y = \dfrac{1}{4}$

(ii) $\dfrac{dy}{dx} = \dfrac{2ax + 4}{(2x + a)^3}$

(iii)

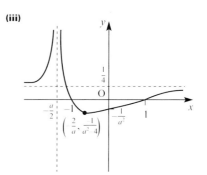

(iv)

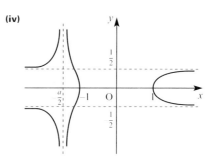

Exercise 6C (Page 142)

1

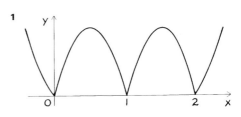

2

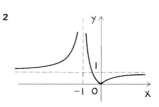

3

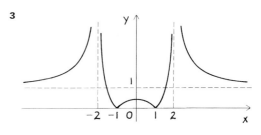

4

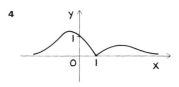

5

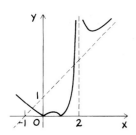

6

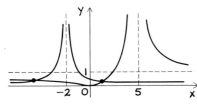

7

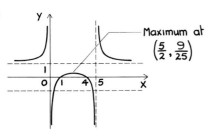

Two roots

8

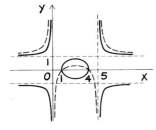

Asymptotes: $x = 0$, $x = 5$, $y = 1$. Nature of stationary point determined by how the curve approaches the asymptotes.

(i)

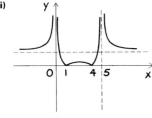

(ii)

9 (i) $\dfrac{\mathrm{d}y}{\mathrm{d}x} = \dfrac{18 - 12x - 6x^2}{(x^2 + 3)^2}$

(ii) $(1, 1)$, $(-3, -3)$

(iii) $y = -2$

(iv)

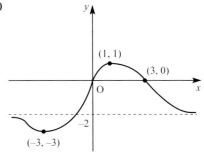

(v)

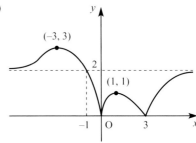

(vi) $x = -1$

Activity (Page 144)

Counter-example: e.g. $5 > 3$ and $4 > 1$ but $5 - 4 < 3 - 1$

Exercise 6D (Page 148)

1 $-3 < x < 1$ or $x > \frac{7}{2}$

2 $x < 1$ or $x > 3$

3 $x < -2$ or $0 < x < 5$

4 $x < -1$ or $2 \leqslant x \leqslant 5$

5 $-1 < x \leqslant \frac{2}{5}$ or $x > 2$

6 $-2 \leqslant x < 0$ or $x \geqslant 4$

7 $x < 3$

8 $x = 0$ or $1 \leqslant x < 2$

9 $-5 \leqslant x < 2$

10 $x < -6$ or $-2 \leqslant x < \frac{2}{3}$

11 $1 \leqslant x \leqslant 3$

12 $-5 \leqslant x \leqslant -\frac{1}{3}$

13 $x > \frac{2}{5}$

14 $-1 \leqslant x \leqslant 2$ or $4 \leqslant x \leqslant 7$

15 $1 \leqslant x \leqslant 3$

16 (i) $-1 < x < 6$

(ii) $x < -1$ or $3 < x < 6$

17 (i) $y = \frac{1}{25}$, $x = \frac{7}{5}$

(ii) $\dfrac{\mathrm{d}y}{\mathrm{d}x} = \dfrac{10 - 14x}{(5x - 7)^3}$

(iii)

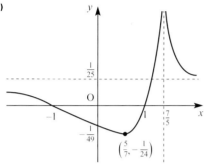

(iv)

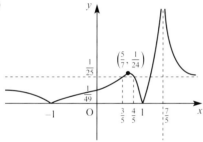

(v) $\frac{3}{5}, \frac{4}{5}, \frac{37}{35}, x < \frac{3}{5}$ or $\frac{4}{5} < x < \frac{37}{35}$

18 (i) $\dfrac{\mathrm{d}y}{\mathrm{d}x} = \dfrac{-14x^2 + 24x - 56}{(x^2 - 4)^2}$

(ii)

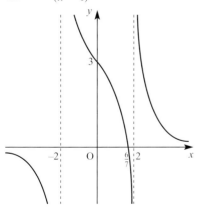

(iii)

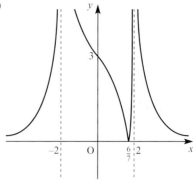

(iv) $-6, \frac{4}{3}$

(v) $x < -6$ or $0 < x < \frac{4}{3}$ or $x > \frac{14}{3}$

19 $x^2(y - 1) + x + 2 = 0$; $8(y - 1) \leqslant 1$; $y \leqslant \frac{9}{8}$

21 $-1 \leqslant y \leqslant 3$

Appendix

❓ (Page 154)

No: $(\mathbf{a}.\mathbf{b}) \times \mathbf{c}$ (the vector product of a scalar and a vector) is meaningless, so $\mathbf{a}.\mathbf{b} \times \mathbf{c}$ is unambiguous.

Exercise (Page 154)

1 (i) -2

(ii) 29

(iii) 0

(iv) 34

2 (iii) W, X, Y, Z are coplanar

3 $(3, 5, 5)$, $(1, 7, 4)$; $\sqrt{117}$ units

4 (i) Area $= \frac{1}{2}|\mathbf{AC}||\mathbf{AB}|\sin A$

(iii) and **(iv)** $24\frac{1}{2}$ units

(v) Method **(i)** involves fewer evaluations of vector products.

5 Yes.

Index